COPING WITH L~

Barbara Baker is a.
Deputy Editor of
freelance Health Edit
writes for many other   ...ul,
self-help and organic 1   ~. ... addition she is
a volunteer telephone s~pporter for the charity Women's
Health.

Barbara lives in Herefordshire with her partner, Martin,
and cat, Lottie. Her passions include t'ai chi, yoga,
walking, as well as TV and radio drama, and she has an
ongoing interest in complementary health approaches. A
recent graduate from the Open University, Barbara has
also gained a Diploma in Health and Social Welfare
Promotion and aims to study for an MA in Food Policy.
Her ambitions are to write a popular television serial
drama, become an organic smallholder, look after a
menagerie of rescued animals and walk from Land's End
to John o' Groats. This is her first book.

Overcoming Common Problems Series

For a full list of titles please contact
Sheldon Press, Marylebone Road, London NW1 4DU

The Assertiveness Workbook
A plan for busy women
JOANNA GUTMANN

Birth Over Thirty Five
SHEILA KITZINGER

Body Language
How to read others' thoughts by their gestures
ALLAN PEASE

Body Language in Relationships
DAVID COHEN

Cancer – A Family Affair
NEVILLE SHONE

Coping Successfully with Hayfever
DR ROBERT YOUNGSON

Coping Successfully with Migraine
SUE DYSON

Coping Successfully with Pain
NEVILLE SHONE

Coping Successfully with Your Irritable Bowel
ROSEMARY NICOL

Coping with Anxiety and Depression
SHIRLEY TRICKETT

Coping with Breast Cancer
DR EADIE HEYDERMAN

Coping with Bronchitis and Emphysema
DR TOM SMITH

Coping with Chronic Fatigue
TRUDIE CHALDER

Coping with Depression and Elation
DR PATRICK McKEON

Curing Arthritis Diet Book
MARGARET HILLS

Curing Arthritis – The Drug-Free Way
MARGARET HILLS

Depression
DR PAUL HAUCK

Divorce and Separation
Every woman's guide to a new life
ANGELA WILLANS

Everything Parents Should Know About Drugs
SARAH LAWSON

Good Stress Guide, The
MARY HARTLEY

Heart Attacks – Prevent and Survive
DR TOM SMITH

Helping Children Cope with Grief
ROSEMARY WELLS

How to Improve Your Confidence
DR KENNETH HAMBLY

How to Interview and Be Interviewed
MICHELE BROWN AND GYLES BRANDRETH

How to Keep Your Cholesterol in Check
DR ROBERT POVEY

How to Pass Your Driving Test
DONALD RIDLAND

How to Start a Conversation and Make Friends
DON GABOR

How to Write a Successful CV
JOANNA GUTMANN

Hysterectomy
SUZIE HAYMAN

The Irritable Bowel Diet Book
ROSEMARY NICOL

Overcoming Guilt
DR WINDY DRYDEN

The Parkinson's Disease Handbook
DR RICHARD GODWIN-AUSTEN

Talking About Anorexia
How to cope with life without starving
MAROUSHKA MONRO

Think Your Way to Happiness
DR WINDY DRYDEN AND JACK GORDON

Overcoming Common Problems

Coping with Long-Term Illness

Barbara Baker

sheldon **PRESS**

Published in Great Britain in 2001 by
Sheldon Press
SPCK
Holy Trinity Church
Marylebone Road
London NW1 4DU

Copyright © Barbara Baker 2001

British Library Cataloguing-in-Publication Data

A catalogue record for this book is available from the British Library

ISBN 0–85969–844–0

Typeset by Deltatype Limited, Birkenhead, Merseyside
Printed in Great Britain by Biddles Ltd
www.biddles.co.uk

This book is dedicated to
my mum, my dad and
my dear brother, Gary

And to Martin and Sharon
for their wonderful love and support.
Thank you.

Contents

Introduction

Who is this book for?

Chronic or long-term illness comes in many forms. There are genetic disorders such as sickle cell anaemia or haemophilia. There are many degenerative diseases ranging from osteoarthritis to motor neurone disease. There are cancers, viruses and bacterial infections ranging from the incurable to the highly treatable. And there is mental illness too.

Some illnesses are widely feared, others are grossly misunderstood, or both. Maybe you suffer from a condition that others do not always take seriously – ME, for example. Not only do you have to try to live your life, day in, day out, in the face of debilitating symptoms, but you may have to deal with other people's scepticism and prejudices too.

Or perhaps you suffer from a condition that is generally perceived by some to be relatively minor – tinnitus or allergies, psoriasis or endometriosis. Yet others often have no idea just how far these so called 'minor' illnesses can affect your life and impact on your everyday sense of well-being.

Perhaps you look well but experience unpleasant symptoms not immediately apparent to those around you. Or you suffer from several different problems. Individually, each one may cause relatively few difficulties – but when stacked up together they begin to take their toll. Even a single minor illness can be debilitating. Most of us know what it is like to suffer from an occasional bout of flu or seasonal hay fever – but what if you suffer from the same annoying symptom all the year round?

Finally, you may be the kind of person who often feels unwell but perhaps you do not know why. Maybe your doctor has said there is nothing wrong with you, yet you feel below par for long periods of time. You may be young or old. People may say that what you are going through is 'normal' for your age, gender, size or given your genetic background. Yet knowing that will not necessarily make you feel better.

The symptoms you experience may be relentless, constant, unremitting; or sporadic, unpredictable and liable to strike at the least convenient moment. You may know you are going to get better one day. For others, the challenge maybe to survive as best you can.

Ultimately, you may be the kind of person who has taken illness in your stride or the kind of person who still cannot believe it has happened to you. Whatever your circumstances, however major or 'minor' your illness, only you really understand how difficult it is, how the symptoms make you feel and how they impact on your life.

In some ways this book may be too ambitious. Every person is an individual, every illness is very different and no two people will experience illness in the same way. But whatever your situation, I hope this book may be a lifeline, a chance to explore how you feel about your illness, an opportunity to find new ways to cope with difficult feelings, and deal with friends, family and the medical profession. It should also provide a valuable resource guide of practical information you can use.

I also hope this book will be of value if you are close to someone who has a chronic illness, and for carers everywhere. Looking after someone who is unwell is an extremely difficult job, but it is hoped this book may offer some fresh insights and support.

I also hope that doctors and nurses will read this book. One study (carried out by Macmillan Cancer Relief, a UK charity which provides support to cancer patients) showed that many cancer patients believe hospital staff could do more to help them cope with their illness. One particular complaint was that patients too often felt like 'a number' rather than an individual. Patients wanted to be given more information about their condition and the treatment they were receiving. When asked what would have improved their experience of cancer, one in six said they had not received the support they needed or the opportunity to talk about the illness with doctors and nurses.

There is no doubt that doctors and nurses do a fantastic job. Undoubtedly, the best nurses and the best doctors take that moment extra to treat patients as people, to see them as individuals with very different needs, fears, worries and anxieties. But above all to listen to their stories. It is so easy to walk past a bed and think you will talk to a patient later, but never get round to it, or assume that another nurse or doctor on another shift will make the effort. Taking a moment to say hello, get to know a patient, hold their hand, if appropriate, listen to them, allay their fears, and treat them as an individual for a few moments – that is the kind of personal medicine that can help people feel better and is so much more rewarding, not just for your patient, but for the health professional too.

INTRODUCTION

A personal note

As the author of this book I am very lucky not to suffer from any major health problems – but I do know what it is like to experience several relentless minor health problems. I know what it is like to feel I should count my blessings but still feel lousy, to feel guilty about moaning but still need a little sympathy, to be afraid of visiting my GP in case I am written off as a hypochondriac, and to cope with those who blithely insist that positive thinking cures everything just because they are lucky enough never to have had any real health problems themselves. I have written about health for many years and received hundreds of heartfelt letters from people who have trusted me with their experiences and helped me understand a little of what it is they are going through. And I have seen serious illness close up with the death of both my dear mum and dad, and a much-loved aunt. My experiences have made me more sympathetic to all kinds of illness – and I hope this book is of some use, especially to those of you who have no one to talk to, no mum or dad to give you a cuddle, and for those who think no one really understands or cares how you feel. This book is written especially for you.

Part 1
Coping with your feelings

1
Understanding Illness

Everyone is different

Being ill can be a very lonely experience. Family members and friends may be supportive and sympathetic but you may still feel that no one really understands what you are going through. However compassionate others are, it can be hard for them to remain constantly caring, especially if you are ill over a long period of time. Ultimately, the only person who truly understands how you feel inside and how your particular symptoms affect your life – is *you*.

It is true that someone else with the same symptoms may respond quite differently – but that does not, or should not, devalue how you feel. We have all been inspired by certain people in the public eye who seem to be able to cope heroically with horrendous medical conditions with humility, humour and amazing resilience and optimism. Sometimes they manage to achieve as much or more than those who are fighting fit! Look at people like Simon Weston, the Falklands veteran who bore terrible injuries with such courage, or Stephen Hawking, the scientist with motor neurone disease now famous for his best-selling book *A Brief History of Time*, or Christopher Reeve, the actor, paralysed after a riding accident but still inspiring others around the world.

But not everyone can bear illness with such obvious courage. Your courage may be much quieter, more private, unobserved by others but just as praiseworthy. On the other hand, you may find it difficult to get out of bed in the morning and struggle to face the day, let alone be an inspiration to anyone else. *Well, that is fine too.*

Inevitably some people who are ill feel guilty. There is so much misery in the world – wars, famine, cruelty, homelessness and so on – that it can seem selfish to focus on one's own difficulties. 'It could

1

be worse', people say. Well, that is true. But it does not mean that you do not feel miserable or that you are not suffering or in pain or that how you feel does not count.

'I know just how you feel'

No one really knows what it is like for you. Certainly, if you have ever been on the receiving end of well-meaning friends who are determined to tell you about someone who is much worse than you but manages to achieve so much more, you will know how annoying it is! And we have all encountered those who, having enquired how you are, quickly announce they know 'just how you feel' because they once suffered from something vaguely similar or their Auntie Jessie, twice removed, had 'exactly the same thing' twenty years ago!

Chances are you will have encountered already people who tell you just to 'think positive', glibly recommend quick-fix diets or promise instant cures. Or those who pretend to care but whose eyes glaze over the moment you try to tell them how you *really* feel. Or even those who are so sympathetic that you end up feeling significantly more miserable than you did before! Worst of all are those (usually the ones who have never been ill in their lives) who imply that if you are ill, somehow it is your fault.

Why me? Why now?

You may find it hard to understand *why* you have become ill. Life can seem so unfair sometimes. Perhaps you have always looked after your body, eaten a good diet, taken regular exercise, followed your doctor's advice and yet still succumbed to illness. Or maybe you have become ill just at a time when it could not be more inconvenient – at the start of a new job, a few weeks after you met the person of your dreams, just as things were beginning to look up for you.

The temptation to ask yourself, 'Why me?' or 'Why now?' is very great. You may feel cheated or drawn to punish yourself with self-recriminations – 'If only I'd done this or that'. Yet it will not change a thing. One of the loneliest aspects of illness is coming to terms with the fact that you may not be able to put the clock back, you cannot magic away symptoms you wish you did not have.

Occasionally, asking, Why me? Why now? can be useful. There are some who can look back and know, to the day, when their illness began, even though the symptoms may not have appeared until some time later. They can pinpoint a particular sequence of stressful events or a set of circumstances when they know they were not looking after themselves as well as they should and feel confident that this was the catalyst for their health problems. As a result they feel able to make positive changes in their lives.

But for others there is no revelation, no clue as to why things have turned out as they have, no sense of a way forward. When that happens, it can test, or break, your faith, because suddenly it can feel as though there is no rhyme or reason to why you became ill. For others, their belief in their God becomes stronger. To those who do not have a faith it can just seem incredibly unfair.

The importance of a diagnosis

It may sound strange, but an important milestone for many people who are ill is to be given a diagnosis. Why should it make a difference? Mandy, 44, explains why it was important for her. For months Mandy had felt unwell but did not know why.

'I hadn't been sleeping very well for ages although I constantly felt tired. I would toss and turn in bed, often waking up with sweat pouring off me, or I'd find myself sleeping on the floor but couldn't remember how I got there. I also felt shaky, my heart was often racing and I was permanently hungry – sometimes I used to get up in the middle of the night and would stuff myself with sandwiches or raid the fridge.

Then my partner started to comment on how bad-tempered I'd become. I'd gone from being a shrinking violet to complaining in restaurants or demanding my money back for shoddy goods. Several times I stormed out of the house after blazing rows, driving off far too fast in a terrible state. I also wrote some terrible letters to some of my friends accusing them of all sorts and I always seemed to be involved in one kind of outburst or another, to the extent that I was warned I might lose my job if I flared up for no reason again. I cried for absolutely no reason and took offence at the slightest thing. Yet throughout it all, I wasn't aware that I was acting abnormally. On the other hand, I couldn't ignore the fact that so many of my friends and family were saying that I didn't seem myself. Eventually people started to say I was paranoid and I began to feel that perhaps I *was* going mad.

When I started to lose weight I convinced myself I had cancer. People were saying I looked gaunt and then on top of everything else I suddenly developed a big lump in my neck – that was when I went to see my GP and he decided to do a blood test.

Suddenly, everything fell into place. It was found I had a highly overactive thyroid and this was causing all my symptoms – the weight loss, insomnia, feeling hot all the time, the hunger, the mood swings, the unpredictable behaviour. I was put on a course of medication immediately. I was told that it might be several weeks or even months before I began to feel better but I didn't care. I was just so glad I knew what was wrong with me. I thought I'd become this horrible person, someone no one liked very much, but getting that diagnosis, knowing that it was my illness that had made me behave that way helped me to feel much better.

Ten years on I still have to take medication so I'm not completely free of the disease but it is under control. I'm so familiar with the symptoms that I know instantly if my thyroid is becoming overactive now and just take myself off to the doctor for a blood test.'

Getting a diagnosis can have many benefits. It can help make sense of the array of symptoms you have. To realize suddenly that you are not alone, that others have experienced the same illness as you or that there is a name for the illness you have may be of some comfort. And it can be a source of optimism too – perhaps others have found ways of coping that you have not yet discovered.

For many, getting a diagnosis means finally being believed. It is confirmation that you really do have a medical condition. Hard, tangible evidence that no one can dispute. It is something you can cling on to when you doubt yourself or when others doubt you.

It may also help others to make more sense of your illness too. If an illness or condition has a name then maybe they will be more sympathetic or understanding! Sometimes a 'label' can help reassure people.

Above all, it gives you a base from which to start to come to terms with, or fight, your illness. If you can find a label or a name for the condition you have then you can start to amass information about how to deal with it, find out about the most up-to-date research, the latest treatments, or talk to others with the same condition.

How to cope if a diagnosis cannot be made

If a diagnosis cannot be made things are a little different. You may already have got used to people demanding to know 'exactly' what is wrong with you. Telling people that you have a 'bad back' but that your GP cannot really tell you why, cuts no ice with some. They reason that if you have not got a specific diagnosis then you cannot really have a problem. At best you are exaggerating. At worst you are making it up. They are not interested in the dozens of times you have been to your GP, the inconclusive X-rays you had, the specialists you have seen. They are not interested in the minutiae of medical detail you could relate or the alternative remedies you have tried. Some are only interested in their own symptoms while others are lucky enough to be so healthy that, understandably, they cannot imagine what it is like to be sick at all!

Yet, even without a diagnosis, you are not alone. There are thousands of people who struggle on with their daily lives feeling below par and feeling that no one understands what they are going through. If you are one of those people, remember that some people do understand. Some people are sympathetic. Even when things seem very bleak, there is always something to aim for. Learning to be your own best friend is a start. But first you have to get to grips with your emotions.

2

A Mixture of Emotions

Discovering you are ill can arouse all kinds of emotions. Of course, it is impossible to generalize – not everyone feels the same and you might find you feel different things on different days or even hour by hour. There could be days you feel strong, able to cope, determined not to let your illness get you down. Yet on other days you may feel fragile, despondent, defeated and worn down. Commonly experienced emotions and feelings include:

- *Numbness* – when you first become ill you may feel numb inside, unable to feel anything much at all. This can be your body's way of protecting you from shock and the sea of emotions welling up inside you.
- *Sadness* – not self-pity but sheer sadness on every level, for the pain you feel and perhaps the now uncertain future you face. Sadness at the loss of good health, the life you had that may now change, sadness for the things you were able to do so easily before but now have to struggle with or cannot do at all. For the things that now seem so precious but perhaps you realise with regret you once took for granted.
- *Disappointment* – at the way your body has let you down, especially if you feel you were leading a relatively healthy life in the first place. Disappointment that you have become ill before you have achieved certain goals or ambitions. Disappointment for the things you can no longer do, the time 'wasted' in doctors' rooms or in hospitals, for all your dashed hopes and dreams.
- *A sense of loss* – in a way it can seem almost like a kind of bereavement, a mourning for the healthy person you used to be, the things you could have achieved, the relationships you might have had if you had been well. You may look at how fit you used to be, the way you used to do things with ease but now find a struggle. In a way, you may feel you have lost a part of you, part of your identity, part of your self-esteem, especially when you find it impossible to do basic things you used to take for granted. You may crave and long to have everything back the way it was.
- *Anger* – that it had to happen to you, you could not stop it happening, that no one can stop the pain, the treatments do not seem to work, perhaps because there is no cure or because people

do not take your illness seriously or say they know 'just how you feel' when clearly they do not have a clue.

- *Self-blame* – wondering if perhaps you could have prevented it, if there was something you did or did not do that contributed to your illness, or if it happened because you are a 'bad' person or deserved it in some way.
- *Frustration* – at diminished physical prowess, at being misunderstood by others, because you long to be normal.
- *Guilt* – for feeling a failure, about the time your illness is 'taking up', the care you need from others, at not being able to fulfil your responsibilities as a wife or husband, as a mother or father, with friends or at work. Or because you know you are sometimes too demanding or feel you do not deserve sympathy. Or because you cannot help wondering if you brought your illness on yourself in some way.
- *Self-pity* – because sometimes you feel so rotten that you *do* feel sorry for yourself – and then feel guilty about that too! Or because there are days when you seem to need to wallow in sympathy.
- *Anxiety* – because you feel out of tune with your body and no longer seem to be in control of what is happening to you. Because you do not know enough about your illness or doctors cannot find anything wrong with you or you feel they do not tell you the truth. Or because you fear those closest to you seem to be getting fed up with you.
- *Fear* – about what the future holds. How will the illness progress? Will you experience pain? Will you ever get better? Supposing you cannot cope? What if friends and family desert you because *they* can no longer cope? Perhaps you are also facing fear about your own mortality for the first time but feel unable to discuss it with anyone or even admit it to yourself.

There are no right or wrong emotions to feel. You feel what you feel. There are no rules. Other people may have their theories or expectations, but you are unique. Only *you* know what it is like for you. Bottling up emotions is definitely a bad idea. It is as though by attempting to drive your feelings underground they become determined to resurface somewhere – but at a price. There is considerable evidence to show that repressing emotions like anger can have a direct impact on your health. For example, there has been research to show that angry people are more likely to have high blood pressure. But even on an everyday level, suppressing emotions and trying to hide what you truly feel takes up a huge amount of energy, leaving you feeling tired, even exhausted. There is some evidence that bottling up your emotions may have a counterproductive effect on your health, not just contributing to stress and anxiety, but stirring up a whole range of physical and emotional symptoms. It may also have a direct effect on your immune system, making you more vulnerable to illness.

But why do so many of us try to hide what we feel? Often it is because we have been brought up that way. As a child, perhaps you were told 'big boys or big girls do not cry'; or lived in an atmosphere where it was considered rude to show dissent, let alone anger, or where it simply 'wasn't done' to show emotions such as sadness or love. But it is no good telling yourself off for feeling self-pity or for feeling anxious or miserable. You have to *feel* the emotion before you can let go of it. Pretending it is not there will not work! Instead, you have to find a safe way to recognize and express what it is you are feeling inside so that it does not consume you and compound the problems you already have.

It may help to realize that what you are feeling is almost certainly normal considering what you are going through. Who would not feel angry if they suddenly find they are in pain or have to give up a job? Who wouldn't feel afraid if they didn't know why they are experiencing certain symptoms or doctors cannot find out what is wrong? Who wouldn't feel sad at the loss of good health? There is nothing bad about such feelings and emotions – they are entirely appropriate given the circumstances.

Confusingly, you may also find that becoming ill has been the catalyst for emotions to surface that are more to do with things that have happened to you in the past, rather than solely to do with what is happening to you now. It can bring to the surface past hurts and disappointments or resentments and recriminations you had almost forgotten about and thought you had dealt with. And to confuse the situation further, you may find that at the onset of illness there is also a curious sense of elation and excitement. This may seem strange but, again, it is a natural reaction that many people experience but rarely talk about – and it is certainly nothing to be ashamed of. This is often due to the simple fact that suddenly there is a lot going on in your life – you may be in and out of medical centres or hospitals and it can be a very busy time so it is easy to 'forget' the reason so much is happening is that you are ill and you get swept along by the frenetic atmosphere instead. The key to all this is to give your feelings and emotions an airing, a chance to work it all through, but how?

Coping with emotions

Learning to face emotions head on is hard and there are no quick fixes, but the following may help:

- *Accept how you feel.* Do not make yourself feel worse because you think you should not feel angry or you should not feel sad. Giving in to how you feel can be the first step to moving on.
- *Try writing down what you feel.* Sometimes we can express in writing what we cannot say in words. Alternatively, try painting a picture. This can seem silly if you have never done it before but it can be a powerful way of getting in touch with what you really feel and you may be surprised at what comes up. It is nothing to do with being able to draw – your picture can be very simple and you may even find that particular colours express what you want to 'say'.
- *Try to find a safe place to express your emotions.* If you are lucky enough to have a supportive partner, or a close friend, make good use of them! Ask them if it is OK if you cry if you feel like crying or shout if you feel like shouting.
- *Find someone to talk to* – for ideas see page 27.
- *If there is a support group* for those suffering an illness like yours, consider joining it. Talking to those who know what you are going through may be an enormous help.
- *Keep a diary of how you feel.* Remember to record entries for the days you feel better and more positive as well as the days you feel lousy. Looking back and realizing there are times when you were able to cope can be beneficial.
- *Try not to look back at what you did or didn't do.* You cannot change the past so accept it for what it is, learn from any mistakes you may have made, and then move on. Feeling guilty achieves nothing.
- *Try to distinguish between old and new emotions.* Are you feeling sad about what is happening to you now – or are sad feelings about what happened to you when you were younger mixed in too? Write down unhappy memories and then if you feel able try symbolically freeing yourself by burning the piece of paper. This sounds a bit New Age-ish and no one is pretending that a simple exercise like this can help solve deep seated problems but you may find it helps a bit.
- *Allow yourself to feel rotten sometimes.* No one can be cheerful all the time. It is natural to feel sorry for yourself from time to time

- *Try to focus as much on what you* can *do as what you cannot do.*
- *Stop trying to be perfect.* Accept yourself for who you are, imperfections included!
- *Plan some good times for yourself* – little treats you will really enjoy.
- *Give yourself praise* when you feel you are making good progress – tell yourself how well you are doing.
- *Accept you will not get it right all the time* – no one does.
- *Forgive yourself for feeling bitter* towards others or jealous of their good health. It is normal to feel like this from time to time.
- *Try outsmarting negative emotions by changing tack.* For example, if you always tend to feel angry towards a certain person because they are not very sympathetic towards you, force yourself to be extra nice towards them and see what it feels like. You may find the process forces a helpful change either in their behaviour or your reaction to it. Adopting a new way of behaving can sometimes help you think differently about a situation too.

Loneliness

Feeling lonely is a very common reaction to illness. The sense of 'why me?' together with the reaction of family and friends who do not always know what to say can leave you feeling isolated. For some, difficulties with mobility, tiredness or anxiety may mean you are no longer physically able or have the confidence to do the things you used to take for granted – shopping or meeting friends, for example. Even if you can get out and about, your illness may make you feel psychologically isolated from others – in the end, it can seem easier just to stay at home.

You can experience inner loneliness even when surrounded by those you love or in a crowded place. This can stem from a feeling that you are alone with your illness, different and separate from those around you in some way. You may not have told everyone about your illness, but it may nevertheless cast a shadow over relationships because you feel that you cannot be 'yourself', but are limited or defined by your illness. Even when others know, and are sympathetic, you can feel alone because, although on the one hand you do want to be understood, at the same time you do not want people's pity and may even resent their sympathy. Above all, you want to be normal – and that, in itself, can contribute to a sense of loneliness.

Getting over loneliness can be difficult because you will have to make an effort especially if others do not even realize how you feel. But even small steps can make a big difference. A phone call, a letter, arranging to meet someone for a coffee, sending an e-mail – if you reach out to others, there is more chance they will reach out to you. You may have to make the first move, but you will be glad you did. Of course, it would be lovely if everyone around you realized just how you were feeling and knew instinctively how to help, but they are only human too and may need a helpful prod in the right direction!

Recognizing depression

Depression is by no means inevitable but some people coping with long-term illness recognize the symptoms all too well. Clinical depression is not just a question of 'going through a bad patch', or being unhappy, though of course that can happen too. It is an illness in its own right – and it can be successfully treated. Unfortunately the Catch-22 of depression is that the more depressed you are, the less likely you are to recognize that you are depressed, which is why it makes sense to talk about your feelings from the outset and tell your doctor how you are feeling so the signs of depression can be picked up at an early stage.

What are the signs of depression? They include:

- feeling negative about everything
- sadness
- bouts of crying
- sleep disturbance – especially waking in the early hours of the morning and being unable to go back to sleep
- apathy and lack of interest in what is going on
- listlessness
- poor appetite
- lack of energy
- headaches or digestive disturbances
- low libido
- feelings of worthlessness, guilt or shame
- being preoccupied by thoughts of death or dying
- thoughts of suicide

Not everyone who is depressed experiences all these symptoms. But if you think you may be suffering from depression, or know someone who is, then it is important to seek medical advice. One reason some people put off seeking help is a fear they will be prescribed tranquillizers which may be addictive. But modern treatments for depression are highly effective and are not addictive. At the very least, have a talk with your doctor and find out what treatments are available. And many of the ideas listed on page 16 can help in the fight against depression too. Take things slowly – do what you can and build on the positive.

The importance of someone to talk to

It can also be invaluable to find someone to talk to. It would be wrong to suggest that there is ever a quick-fix for depression but talking about how you feel can be of enormous help. Some organizations, such as the Samaritans, provide 24-hour support – all you have to do is pick up the phone. Or you may consider that talking to a counsellor even for a limited number of sessions could be therapeutic. See Resources (page 107) for information. You may have always shunned the notion of counselling but it can be a lifeline in certain circumstances. At the simplest level, just to tell someone how you feel, tell them your story, can be incredibly beneficial – a great way of offloading and helping you to recharge your batteries sufficiently to carry on. But it can also be a chance to work through your feelings in greater detail, learn more about yourself than you expected and give you fresh insights into how you might go forward.

But opening up to a close friend or someone you trust can be just as helpful if you are lucky enough to have someone who will listen. When you are ill, it is not very often that you have the chance to say how you really feel. Quite a lot of the time you are probably 'putting on a brave face', trying to be positive for the sake of your partner or your children, or keeping your deepest feelings private, either to protect others, to protect yourself or to keep up appearances – for example to avoid being seen as a 'whinger'. But if you do have the opportunity to let rip, then take it! It is not selfish to want to be heard. Just offloading how you feel can be of enormous help – and other people may be able to offer useful insights you have not thought of before.

How friends and family feel

It is important to say that if your illness has been a shock to you, then it is almost certainly a shock to your friends and family too and they will be going through many of the emotions you are going through. Discovering that someone you love is ill, and that you cannot do anything to 'make it all better' or take away the pain, is a very sad and often frightening experience. You may find that some of those you thought would rally round act in an unexpected way, by seeming to shun you or avoid talking about your illness. This is very unlikely to be because they do not love you but because they simply do not know how to handle their fear. In a way, they may be going through a kind of 'mourning' process – it is almost as though they are grieving for you, for the loss of the way things were for you and because they are so sad for you. Chances are they have always found it difficult to show their emotions openly so they are embarrassed. Perhaps they are worried they will break down, cry, upset you or say the wrong thing. They may even be afraid of the powerful emotions your illness has evoked in them and feel in turmoil or at a loss to know how to react. It may seem they are being unbelievably cruel by reacting like this but it may be the only way they know how to protect themselves.

Sometimes it is hard to imagine this can be what the other person is feeling, especially if they seem cold and distant on the outside. But chances are they feel in turmoil on the inside, afraid, bursting with emotion, gripped by sadness and fear and at a loss to know what to say to you. It may seem ironic, but at this time *you* may need to reach out and help *them*. Even saying something simple like, 'It is all right. I know this is difficult for you. Let's just sit together for a while' can help to break the ice. This may not be easy if you are struggling to come to terms with your own feelings and emotions. But if you can keep open the communication lines at this point, it will help you both.

3
Self-Image and Self-Esteem

When illness strikes it can severely affect the way you view yourself. If you have been relatively well all your life and then become ill, it can be a terrible shock. Suddenly all your perceptions about yourself may have to change. You might feel your body has let you down, that it no longer functions in the way you are used to. Little things you used to take for granted become hugely significant. You become aware of your body in ways you never were before. And other people react to you differently too – you may become someone they have to make allowances for, someone to pity, someone they have to treat with kid gloves. Or perhaps they simply do not understand on any level what the problem is or what your illness is like for you.

How illness can affect your self-esteem

Small changes in physical ability can have significant impact on how you see yourself. For years you have taken for granted a million things you do without thinking – getting out of a chair, making a cup of tea, reaching up to brush your hair, bending down to pick something up, getting into a bath, writing a cheque. Finding you can no longer do some of these things without a real effort, or that they are beyond your capability altogether, is a tremendous blow to your confidence. Some people may feel a kind of loss akin to bereavement with emotions ranging from acute sadness to anger.

Even more adjustment may need to be made if there is a change in your physical appearance or visible signs of your illness. All your life you have taken for granted that you look a certain way, so if you suddenly find you look different it can be very distressing.

You may be lucky enough to know that the physical difficulties you are having are temporary – but it may still be hard to adjust. Others may try to reassure you that you look all right, some may lie to you and say they do not notice your new appearance when you feel sure they do. But equally they may be telling the truth. Perhaps they genuinely do not notice – because ultimately you are the same person underneath. It is the inner you, your personality, your warmth, your character, your idiosyncrasies, even your annoying faults, they see!

'I don't tell anyone about my illness because I do not want them to pity me,' says Margaret, 35, who has been suffering from pernicious anaemia for over 20 years. 'If people pitied me then it would confirm my worst fear, that I am ill – and I do not want to see myself as an ill person. Then, at least, if I am having a good day I can pretend to myself that I'm healthy, that I'm normal like everyone else.'

For some, it is not possible to do that because their illness is highly visible. If your physical appearance changes as a result of your illness it can be upsetting and dent your confidence.

Lack of confidence

Your confidence can also be shaken by the fact that people who you once considered friends cannot handle your illness. They may not believe that you really are ill or are just fed up because they think they have to be sympathetic or make allowances for you. In the end they may find it easier to allow the friendship to drift than make the effort to stay in touch.

Many people have a kind of mental 'hierarchy' of illnesses. Top of the list may be things like cancer or a heart attack. Those at the bottom of the list might include illnesses they do not understand or have no experience of, or those that appear to outsiders to be quite minor. Such attitudes or prejudices or misguided judgements are not necessarily malicious or deliberately unkind but borne out of ignorance. Knowing this, however, does not necessarily make it easier for you to cope. If you sense by what someone says, or does not say, that they do not take your illness very seriously, think you are over-reacting, making a fuss, exaggerating, or seeking attention, it can seriously dent your self-esteem.

Above all, you may crave to be heard, long for someone to listen to what it is like for you. It does not seem much to ask yet can be impossible to achieve, wearing you down and making it more likely that, in the end, you fear you might become the person others may have written you off as. You do not want to be someone who complains all the time or who moans about symptoms, but when no one listens or seems to care it can feel as though you are turning into the very person you do not want to be, eroding your confidence again.

How to boost your confidence

Being ill can have a devastating effect on your confidence. Whether it is the physical limitations, the emotional toll the illness takes, the impact on your relationships, or a combination of all of these, your confidence can feel as though it has taken a battering. The following may help:

- Focus on what you can do, rather than what you cannot.
- Think about all the things in your life you have achieved. You do not need to climb Mount Everest – being a parent, bringing up decent kids, being good at your job, not giving up, having a nice home, learning a new skill, being a kind person – these are all things you can be genuinely proud of.
- Mentally give yourself praise when you do something well – a metaphorical pat on the back. This can seem silly but it is very therapeutic, particularly if you live alone or do not have anyone close to you to give you positive feedback.
- If you do have friends or family who give positive feedback or make you feel good about yourself, spend more time with them!
- Never put yourself down – we all get into the habit of criticizing or poking fun at ourselves, even if it is just to get a laugh. But even jokey attempts to belittle yourself can have the effect of denting your confidence. In addition, others may misconstrue it as an attempt to gain sympathy.
- Do something new or something you have always wanted to do. Whether it is writing a poem, joining an art class, reading up about archaeology or getting to grips with the internet. Do not put it off any longer. Put your plan into action now!

Boost your self-image, boost your self-esteem

So is there anything you can do to make yourself feel better about your body when it seems to have let you down? The overwhelming thing to remember is that you are still YOU inside. Try to see your body as an outer shell. It is a part of you but it is not *all* of you, it does not define you, it does not reflect your personality or say anything about all the qualities you have. It is merely one layer of a very complex individual. It does not tell the whole story. It is true that some people may be too shallow, too embarrassed or too afraid to look beneath the surface – but that is their problem.

In the same way that you might see your body is just one layer of you, the person inside, it can be helpful to see your illness as just one layer of your life. The more new layers you build into your life, the less dominant the illness may seem. What kind of layers? It depends on the severity of your illness and how much you can manage. One example is finding a new interest, something new to get involved in. Again, is there something you have always longed to have a go at – writing or pottery? If you feel very unwell or have severe mobility problems even the simplest lifestyle changes can give you a fresh perspective – listening to a different radio station. It sounds absurdly simplistic – but it might just provide something new to talk about or look forward to. That does not mean your illness is any less severe than it was. It does not negate your experience so far, the difficulties you have had or the suffering you have experienced. You are not denying any of that. But building in new layers to your life can help change your outlook and make life more enjoyable.

At the other end of the spectrum, finding a new interest can give you newfound confidence and take your mind off the symptoms that sometimes get you down. What is going on in your local area? What groups could you join? Who could you telephone? It is easy to discard every suggestion and think, 'I do not want to try that', but maybe it would be worth giving something new a chance?

4
Living Day by Day

Most changes we make in our life are changes we intended to make – a house or job move for example. Changes that are forced upon us, especially those that happen suddenly, can be much more difficult to cope with. Not least because you have no time to adjust to what is happening or prepare for the various ways it may impinge on your life.

Accepting life may never be the same again is one of the hardest things of all. It is tempting to look back to how things used to be when you were well, when you could do what you wanted, when you wanted. You can probably remember the time you took for granted simple tasks you now find difficult.

Make the most of every day

Learning to live in the present is not easy – but can make a big difference to how well you cope with your illness. So how can you begin to make the adjustment and learn to make the most of every day? These ideas may help:

- *Let go of the past*. That does not mean you have to blank out all your good memories, but if looking back is stopping you accepting your current state of health, makes you feel angry about current limitations, or prevents you from living life to the full today, then perhaps it is time to put the past on one side for a while. It may help to think of it rather like closing an old photograph album and shutting it away in a drawer. Looking back may give you a genuine source of comfort, but if not, wait until you feel stronger.
- *Do not waste time wishing things had turned out differently*. Put all your energy into making today as good as it can be.
- *Take each day on its merits*. If you have a 'good' day, then try to make the most of it, but do not be so eager to overcompensate that you tire yourself out. Take things at a steady pace.
- *Keep a diary so you can record 'good' days and 'bad' days*. Make a note of achievements you are pleased with – be pleased with 'minor' accomplishments as well as any major ones.

18

- *Think of an ongoing project* you could tackle on days when you feel up to it. It might be something like knitting a jumper, painting a picture, completing a jigsaw, writing about your childhood, researching a family tree, making a simple piece of furniture, embroidering a cushion, writing your autobiography, making a frieze of your child's pictures, or stitching a quilt. Choose something you are interested in that is challenging or relaxing but also enjoyable and above all within your capability – something you can easily pick up when you are feeling well and put aside when you are not. Each time you work on it, you will see a little more progress. Focus on what you have achieved, rather than what remains undone.
- *Acknowledge any advantages as well as the limitations your illness brings.* Adopting a lighthearted approach to this can help avoid negativity – even if it is just joking to friends that at least you can watch daytime TV.
- *Redefine your priorities.* What is important to you now? It is not selfish to put yourself first – it is a matter of self-preservation. That might mean that you want to spend more time, effort and resources on eating a good diet, experimenting with alternative therapies or simply getting through each day. It may mean you have less energy left to do things for other people.
- *Set realistic goals.* Devising a clear set of goals can give you something to work towards, targets to aim for and achievements to look back on and be proud of. A mixture of short-term, medium- and long-term goals is ideal. A short-term goal might be to go for a very short walk every afternoon or joining a self-help group. A long-term goal might be writing about your experiences, getting a job, taking a course or learning to drive.
- *Time-plan your day if it would be helpful.* Spending a couple of minutes each morning making a 'To Do' list cuts down on worry time later on wondering what you should be doing.
- *Prioritize tasks* so that you tackle the most urgent things first – leave anything that can wait until tomorrow.
- *Do not take on more than you can comfortably manage* and leave time in your day for unexpected problems and delays.
- *Accept your limitations.* If you cannot fit everything in, be prepared to let go. Look at it like this – giving others the chance to take more responsibility does not mean you have failed. It is a key aspect of being a good parent, friend or partner. Bear in mind that others may relish the chance to take on more responsibility.
- *Key in time for YOU!* Do not get into the habit of thinking you

will go swimming or laze in the bath 'if you have time'. Make a conscious effort to *plan* that time into your diary so you do not feel constantly that you are the least important member of the family. Your needs are as important as everyone else's!

- *Do unpleasant tasks first* so you get them out of the way. Capitalize on good days by doubling up on tasks whenever you can. For example, if you feel well enough to do some cooking, why not bake one pie for tonight and another for the freezer.
- *Learn how to say 'no'* so that you do not end up spending time attending events you would rather not go to or agreeing to things just because you are afraid of hurting someone's feelings.
- *Invest in an answerphone* so you can choose when you speak to people.
- *Be prepared to delegate more* – ensure no one gets stuck with the most boring job and consider paying your children extra pocket money in return for doing chores. Tell yourself it is character-building for them!
- *Try to live in the 'here and now'* rather than worry too much about the past or the future.

How to deal with negative thoughts

The sheer relentlessness of being chronically ill can sometimes make it hard to stay positive, and there are bound to be days when negative thoughts drift into your mind. So how can you tackle this?

- When you are finding it particularly hard to cope, allow yourself a 'misery' ten minutes every day. This is the time you can really let rip with all your frustrations, pain, anger and other negative emotions. Allow yourself to rant and rave, punch a cushion, moan at your partner, phone a friend to offload or write down how you feel – and then STOP. Getting into the habit of 'saving up' the worst of how you feel for a short but concentrated period of time can help prevent a general feeling of discontent and malaise that drags on throughout the day.
- If you are troubled by worries at night, and tend to suffer sleepless nights as a result, make a list of exactly what you are worried about and resolve to deal with them in the morning. The sheer act of writing out a list is a mysterious process and somehow a positive step that can help you put worries to one side – leaving them 'on ice' as it were – and allow you to have a better night's sleep.

- Consider the idea that the biggest difficulty in your life is not that you are ill, but how you think about your illness. You can see it in purely negative terms, dwell on the worst aspects and most depressing symptoms, the limitations, the disadvantages – or you can focus on the positive elements of your life.
- You cannot always stop negative thoughts coming into your mind, but you do have a choice as to whether you allow them to fester.
- To a great extent, being negative is a habit, a learned response. When negative thoughts come, gently push them away as you would with any intrusive thought that arrives at the wrong moment. Allow yourself to feel that you are in charge of negative thoughts. They are not in charge of you and you control whether or not you want to dwell on them. If they persist, have a nice thought ready to replace the negative thought with. For example, imagining yourself lying on a sun-drenched beach or doing something you enjoy.
- Try little 'tricks' that work for you. For example, when you get into bed at night, you may find that worries flood into your mind. One way to deal with them is to have a 'worry' side and a 'definitely no worrying' side. Lie on your 'worry' side for the first five minutes and let the negative thoughts come and go. Then turn on your 'definitely no worrying' side. The action of turning over is like turning your back on your worries. Be determined that you never worry on your 'do not worry' side! This simple trick is surprisingly effective.
- Do not generalize in a negative way – just because you had a bad experience on a previous occasion does not mean you will have a bad experience every time.
- Bear in mind that you may be locked into a spiral of negative thinking simply because it is a pattern familiar to you. If you were brought up in an atmosphere where your parents tended to think the worst, you may well have grown up with the same attitudes and never questioned them. But ask yourself where is the evidence for the way you think? It may once have been a helpful attitude – but is it helpful to you now? Or is it an unhelpful attitude that is creating anxiety, holding you back or even contributing to your illness?
- Do not always assume the worst. It can make you feel hopeless – and helpless – about everything and contribute to depression.
- Do not overdramatize when something goes wrong or you make a mistake. If you consistently blow things out of proportion you will end up only focusing on the negative.

- Do not waste time thinking of regrets. If only I had not become ill, if only I were better – it will not change what has happened so concentrate your energy on how you can make your life better *despite* your illness.
- When you find yourself catastrophizing about what might happen, ask yourself what evidence you have for making negative assumptions. Are there other more realistic, positive consequences you could focus on instead?

Part 2
Coping with family and friends

5
Friends and Family

There are almost as many reactions to illness as there are illnesses and it is not always easy to predict how people will respond – even if you think you know them well. It is extremely upsetting and disappointing if someone close to you is negative or non-supportive. If someone accuses you of exaggerating your illness or even of 'wanting' to be ill, or tries to trivialize what you are going through or cannot be bothered to send you a card when you are in hospital, it can be extremely hurtful. At times of crisis, most people rely on their family for support and if that support is lacking or non-existent then illness can be a very lonely, isolating place.

When you are ill, you are bound to feel more vulnerable than usual and little gestures can mean so much. When I had to go into hospital for a hysterectomy, all my friends were wonderful, but my best friend Sharon sent me a card and a gift – usually something to make me laugh – every single day. Just knowing she was thinking of me and had bothered to go to all that trouble, even though she was so busy, made such a tremendous difference to my morale and also to my determination to make a speedy recovery. Her fantastic kindness and absolute support is something I will never forget and, in turn, has made me realize how much such gestures can mean to others.

Some people see getting ill in the first place as a kind of weakness. There is a current vogue for 'taking responsibility' for your health. This is great in some ways. If you can eat healthily, give up smoking, take regular exercise and manage to stay healthy as a result, then that is wonderful. But some people do all those things and become ill anyway. Others do not manage to lead a healthy lifestyle and as a result are blamed when things go wrong as though they 'deserve' to be ill. There are some who take a trendy New Age line that, somehow you actually 'want' to be sick for some deep-seated psychological reason. Again, many of these theories are bandied about by those who have never experienced illness themselves and have limited capacity to empathize with others, or who misunderstand the very 'theories' they are keen to expound. No doubt if those who are quick to judge and blame others ever become ill themselves, they will declare that they are the exception to their rule, that they did not want to be and do not deserve to be ill and that it is not their fault. It is a shame they cannot view other people who become ill with the same kind of empathy.

You may find other people's reactions irritating when in fact all they are trying to do is help! If you are trying to explain how you feel and are regaled with statements such as 'I know just how you feel' when clearly the other person doesn't have a clue, or 'That's funny – I get all those symptoms too' when they obviously do not, it can be exceedingly annoying! It is the equivalent parody of the sick person lying in the hospital bed and the visitor who eats all their grapes! It is best at these times to remember that, however irritating, the other person is probably doing their level best to be sympathetic. By telling you that they understand or know what it is like to have a certain symptom they are trying to empathize in the best way they can. They probably do not know what else to say and they are at least trying to make you feel better. It is best to accept what they say at face value and with good grace.

Surprisingly, it can also be irritating if someone is overly sympathetic! If someone offers *too* many comforting words, understanding looks and caring body language, it can be almost as annoying as someone who ignores your distress altogether! Yet it can also be helpful, or at least a catalyst for change – a bit like seeing yourself in a new light and realizing that you do not actually want to be the kind of ill person that provokes such reactions in others. (Some people might even find this book has the same effect!)

Illness changes relationships. It changes the dynamics between people. What may once have worked because it was an equal relationship can falter because now there is an imbalance if you are needier than you were before. Maybe you cannot join in as many activities as you used to. Perhaps friends took it for granted before that you would meet up for a drink, play squash, or go swimming at a moment's notice but maybe now you have to say no because you feel too tired or unwell. True friends will understand and give you the support and space you need – but some may be annoyed or think you are not trying hard enough, that you are attention-seeking or that the friendship has become one-sided.

Sandra, 53, had to give up her job as a primary school teacher in

1995 due to serious health problems which have included viral pneumonia, ME, candida, adrenal problems and an underactive thyroid: 'I was suffering from severe fatigue to the point where I just didn't realize how slowly I was speaking, moving and thinking. I just sat on the settee and time seemed to last hundreds of years. In my quiet world I saw, but noticed nothing.' Throughout Sandra has found it difficult to get a proper diagnosis and feels she has not always been treated sympathetically by the medical profession. But she has also found that some friends were less than supportive too. 'Some friends fell by the wayside because they could not accept that I am ill, not least because I often look quite well and healthy. They do not realize how difficult it is for me to socialize – but then they have not seen me when my energy levels are at their worst, when I am taking ages to get up and dressed, or have breakfast or do the kind of things we all normally take for granted. I am so thankful for the good friends I have, the ones who understand what it is like for me, the ones who know I am ill. I try to be positive because I'm determined to get better. No one wants to be ill. In some ways, the reactions of some of my friends have helped me to become tougher. I have to look after myself and I am lucky enough to have a supportive family. But when my energy reserves are low I save them to help myself get better, count my blessings and focus on the good friends I have.'

Misunderstandings can arise if you make too many assumptions. Do not automatically assume others know what you are going through – how can they know if you do not tell them? You could notice some unexpected reactions too. Some people may seem jealous at all the attention your illness is getting. You may find there is someone close to you who is determined to be the only person you turn to during illness and so resents it if you allow others to help you. Some will start to treat you like a child, as though you cannot make decisions for yourself, trying to act as 'gatekeeper' in terms of who you should see or where you should go, etc. Or take it upon themselves to try to talk to doctors on your behalf as though you are not capable of doing it yourself. Often, all these reactions are the result of good intentions. If someone is overly protective towards you it may be because they love you and want the best for you. But if it feels uncomfortable then you must gently explain how it makes you feel.

Equally you may feel that people react differently to you once they know you are ill, treating you almost as though you are a china doll or a child. You might feel that, where once they would have nagged you or shouted at you or spoken their mind, suddenly they are holding back and being overly nice. You can find yourself longing for a good row instead of being 'humoured' all the time. On the other hand, you may develop a new closeness with some members of your family or some friends which sustains you through the bad days. Perhaps you will have the chance to talk about your feelings and emotions in a deeper way than ever before – and both benefit from a deeper understanding and appreciation of each other.

Tips on dealing with friends and family

Many difficulties can be resolved if you are able to talk about them, share your feelings and allow others to share theirs. Here are some ideas which may help.

- *Explain everything you can about your illness* – the symptoms you have, how it makes you feel, what you can and can no longer do, so they are fully aware of the situation.
- *Be clear about what you need.* If you need time on your own or you need extra time to sleep, do not assume they know. If they understand why, chances are they will be more willing to co-operate.
- *Avoid talking about your illness all the time.* You may find that you do not talk about it at all with some friends or family members but it is the primary topic of conversation with others. It is a natural reaction to 'make the most' of those who are able to discuss it with you, but beware of seeming to take advantage of those who are too polite or nice to object!
- *Be aware that friends and family have needs too.* If the balance of your relationship has changed, they may feel you are getting all the attention and feel left out. Try to redress the balance on the days when you feel better by asking how they are, being the one to initiate a phone call, or day out, or surprise gift.
- *Get organized.* Have a stock of birthday cards and stamps ready to use in case on the day you planned to buy one you are feeling too poorly to make the effort. Make the most of good days so you can think ahead and avoid a situation where you are accused of not responding to others' needs.
- *Accept that not everyone will understand what you are going*

26

through. Some people will be unsympathetic or cross to the other side of the street when they see you coming because they do not know what to say. Bear in mind your illness may provoke uncomfortable feelings or memories they are not aware of, do not understand or cannot articulate. If you feel well enough, try to build bridges. Tell the person perhaps in a letter that you miss their company, you care for them and you would like to see them and then wait for a response. It may be the prompt they are waiting for. Inevitably you may lose contact with some but try not to feel bad about that. You cannot control what other people think or how they feel. You need to conserve your energy to help you cope with your own situation.

Maintaining a social life and finding new interests

Depending on your illness and how far it impinges on your daily life, you may have to make big adjustments to your social life but it is important not to abandon it altogether. You might need to drop certain activities altogether – especially the adventurous or more physically demanding ones – but be open-minded about alternatives.

- If you are mainly confined to home, consider getting wired up to the Internet. Even if you are not very technologically minded, it is much easier to 'surf the net' than you think and it can open up a whole world of possibilities – new interests, fascinating websites, access to discussion groups on every topic under the sun, as well as keeping you totally up to date with what is happening both at home and abroad in every field, from general news to sport, the environment to show business.
- If you cannot get out, ask people to come to you. Even if you can do very little for yourself, there is no reason why others cannot bring food and drink and get involved in debating a hot topic, having a picnic in the lounge, or watching a film together.
- The important thing is to do what you can. If you cannot get out, perhaps you can phone or write a letter, send a card or postcard or send an e-mail? Just keep in touch.

Making new friends

It is difficult, but not impossible, to make new friends when you are ill. An obvious starting point is a local self-help group, if there is one, where you can meet others who share your illness and know what you are going through. If there is a national charity devoted to your illness, this is your best starting point. Or look at local notice-boards to see what is going on. You could also consider putting a small advertisement in your local newspaper. Protect your safety in the first instance by arranging a box number so you can screen replies and ascertain they are genuine.

When you do find yourself in a situation with new people, one of the biggest problems many people find is making small talk. There are four main reasons why you might find small talk difficult: fear of saying the wrong thing; fear of being boring; fear of asking a stupid question; or worries that you will appear unintelligent. Underpinning these fears is usually a lack of confidence. Somehow you feel that what *you* have got to contribute is unimportant. Consequently, your response may simply be to stay silent or, worse, to avoid social situations altogether.

So how can you break the pattern? Do not assume when you look around a roomful of strangers everyone there is bristling with confidence except you. The reality is that at least a few of the other people in any given situation feel a bit awkward, shy and tongue-tied. Even those who seem at ease chatting may not be as self-assured as you imagine. People react to stress in different ways. Some people clam up – others talk too much!

Think about how *you* react to what others say. If someone comments on the weather or asks you where you live, do you immediately judge them as being boring? Of course not! If someone chats about nothing in particular do you think they are stupid? You probably do not. You are more likely to be grateful to them for at least making the effort.

How to make small talk

Learning to make 'small talk' can be a useful way of relaxing into a conversation – but how do you do it?

- *Practise in a safe place.* Try starting a conversation with the person behind you in the supermarket queue or the woman sitting next to you in the hospital waiting-room and you will feel more confident in a situation where you would normally feel nervous.
- *Start with low-risk icebreakers.* Talking about the weather may seem predictable, but it is safe and something everyone can chat about.

- *Ask questions.* Such as, where the other person lives. You might ask how long they have lived there and what they like about the place. Ask 'open-ended' questions – a question that requires a full answer rather than just a 'yes' or 'no'.
- *Listen carefully to the other person's answers* – and follow up with another question. This sounds obvious but all too often we do not listen properly to what other people say, either because we are nervous or we are already panicking about or preparing what we are going to say next. If you listen carefully, you will invariably be given a nugget of information you can follow up. Listen also for tone of voice as that may give you a clue about the person's attitude about a topic.
- *Find some common ground* – especially in the early stages of a conversation. Perhaps you loved and he hated the movie you are discussing, but maybe you both enjoyed the music or admired one of the actresses involved?
- *Don't ask personal questions too soon.* It may be seen as a bit threatening.
- *Admit you do not know what to say.* Sometimes making a simple statement about how you feel will help: 'I always feel a bit shy in large groups and find it difficult to think of things to say.' Chances are the other person will admit they feel the same.
- *Express your opinion about a topical issue* – 'I was amazed to read that . . .'
- *Ask for the other person's opinion* – 'What do you think about the latest . . .'
- *Be aware of your body language.* If you sit tight-lipped, cross-legged, with your arms crossed and your eyes downcast, then you should not be surprised if no one comes up to talk to you! Use friendly body language to help others get the message that you are approachable.
- *Make eye contact.* Keep an open posture and smile, lean forward when the other person is talking, nod appropriately, etc. If you send out friendly messages, you will get friendly messages back.
- *Give verbal clues* to show you are listening and encourage the conversation forward: 'Uh, huh', 'I see', 'Really?', 'What happened then?', etc.
- *Focus on the other person.* People who are shy and unconfident in social situations tend to focus almost exclusively on themselves and how they are feeling instead of the other people in the room. By switching focus and concentrating on what the other person is saying and feeling, you will automatically feel less self-conscious.

Remember that we all love to talk about ourselves. A trick is to start your questions with 'How', 'Why', 'What' or 'Where'.

- *Use reflective listening techniques.* A good trick to move a conversation on is to carefully listen to what the other person says and 'reflect it back' to them. So, if the other person says, 'I was in New York the other week', you could say, 'Oh, you were in New York?' It sounds silly, but it is like batting the ball back into their court and sufficient to prompt the other person to say something else. It is also a good technique if you really cannot think of anything to say!

- *Stop 'monitoring' yourself.* If you try to rehearse everything you are going to say or worry about how you are saying it and the effect it is having on others, then you cannot be spontaneous. The censor in your head will edit what you want to say before the words are even out of your mouth. The result? You will come across as stilted and inhibited. What you are actually trying to do is keep control of the situation – but the reality is you cannot! Topics you had not planned for will inevitably come up and if you cannot relax a little and just see what happens, you simply will not enjoy yourself. Accept from the start that, from time to time, you will say the wrong thing or your conversation will be less than sparkling. The point is that no one is perfect – it really does not matter!

- *Do not be afraid to admit you do not know something.* You are not expected to be psychic, so if you do not understand something the other person is telling you, ask for clarification. A simple 'I've never heard of that before, could you explain what it is?' or 'That sounds interesting. Could you tell me a bit more about it?' or 'I didn't understand the last bit of what you said, could you explain it again?' will not make you look silly, but will enable you to take the conversation forward. People will think you are wonderful simply because you are taking the trouble to find out more about them!

- *Remember you cannot expect everyone to like you.* Also, just because someone does not agree with your views, does not mean they dislike you! If you worry too much about getting others to see your point of view then you will be spending less time listening to their point of view!

- *Take things slowly* at first until the friendship gets under way.

- *Do not expect more than you can give.*

- *Keep in touch by phone or letter* when you do not feel like going out.

Above all, when meeting new people do not assume they are bristling with confidence – they probably feel as nervous as you do.

6

You and Your Partner

When you are in the midst of a long-term illness, it affects not just you, but those around you too – and often it is your partner who is most in the firing line! You may put on a brave face for other members of your family, and for friends, but your partner is the one most likely to see you with your mask down.

If you have a good relationship, your partner is likely to be your primary source of support. He or she will most closely understand what it is you are going through, the minutiae of how the illness affects you. They will know the difference between your 'good' and 'bad' days, what you can do and what you cannot. They will often know instinctively how you are feeling, when you are in pain or when you are feeling sorry for yourself! If you are lucky, they will pamper you when you are feeling low, cheer you up when you are down, make excuses for you when you do not want to see anyone, and even fight some of your battles for you. If you are lucky enough to have a partner like that, great.

On the other hand, maybe your partner is less than perfect! Perhaps he or she tries to be supportive but finds it very difficult. Maybe you feel they *do not* really understand at all, they try to cheer you up when you would rather be left alone, or never make allowances for how you feel.

Understanding your partner's feelings

It may be your partner does not know *how* to react. They may want to be supportive, but find it incredibly hard to know what to do or say. Things are left unsaid and misunderstandings easily arise. You might take their silence as being resentment, or see it as uncaring. They might see the fact you never explicitly ask for help or sympathy as a sign you do not need any! Or maybe your partner does not even try to be supportive or is actively hostile – leaving you feeling that you are enduring your illness quite alone.

Recognizing that your partner has needs too is hard. If you have suddenly become ill then he or she has to make almost as many adjustments and changes as you have had to. Their hopes and dreams may have been dashed as well as yours, and they may be valiantly trying to hide their sadness and frustration from you. Roles within the relationship are bound to have changed too – if you once took the lead or you were the confident, outgoing type and your partner was content in taking a back seat, perhaps those roles have reversed and, like you, your partner has been plunged into an unfamiliar role that seems uncomfortable.

Your partner may find it very difficult to see you in pain or suffering or miserable. Like you, they may constantly be wishing things were as they used to be, frustrated they cannot wave a magic wand to make it all better.

In fact you may have more in common at this time than you think. Your partner may be going through similar emotions – sadness, guilt, anger or fear – about what has happened. Guilt because they didn't foresee what was happening or didn't 'make' you go to the doctor earlier, or because they know they are not doing their fair share of looking after you. Anger that it has disrupted your life together, that it is untimely in some way. Perhaps they wanted to put all their efforts into their career at the moment but feel torn because they also feel obliged to care for you. Or they might feel cheated because this is the time you should have been retiring and had more leisure time together but instead you have to spend endless hours in doctors' surgeries or in hospital waiting-rooms so you cannot fulfil all the hopes and dreams you shared, or do all the things you planned after all. They may also feel a deep sense of fear about what the future holds. Will you become sicker? Will it always be like this? Will they be able to cope? and so on.

It is easy to convince yourself that because you are the one who is ill, then your partner must take second place, they have to fit in around you and you should take priority because you are having such an awful time. Yet however ill you are, you cannot expect to take priority all the time. It is essential to find a balance within the relationship that works for *both* of you and addresses *both* your individual needs and your needs as a couple.

What to do

So what can you do to help your relationship through this difficult phase?

- *Talk about how you feel* – and get your partner to express their thoughts and emotions too. Men may find it more difficult to express their feelings than women.
- *Do not assume he or she knows how you feel.* Do not rely on the other person's intuition or powers of observation.

- *Be explicit about your feelings*, so there is no misunderstanding.
- *Ask about what is going on in your partner's life* – work, friends, interests. Keep in touch with the small details.
- *Spend private time together* – even if it is just a quiet night in listening to music.

A sexual life together

Many illnesses inevitably disrupt one's sexual life. This may be due to the illness itself or to certain medication you may be taking. Your illness may have raised issues about your self-image or dented your self-esteem. Or you may be putting so much effort and energy into coping day-to-day that you have no energy left for sex. For others, sex may be the last thing on your mind. You just do not feel like it and any approach by your partner is seen as an invasion of your personal space.

Problems arise when your need and desire for sex is very different from your partner's. If your partner craves a sexual life, and you do not, there is bound to be conflict, unspoken resentment or hurt feelings, unless you both make the effort to discuss these issues and keep the lines of communication open between you. Remember that you do not necessarily have to have sex in order to feel close. So many couples make the mistake of shutting off all physical contact because they are afraid that even a cuddle might be construed as an invitation to sex. Misunderstandings can arise – but are less likely if you talk your feelings through. This can be very difficult for some people. If you have never openly discussed sex together, then it can be hard to suddenly bring it into the conversation. But avoiding the issue will not make it go away and will only add to the stress and strain you feel about the situation.

If you can, try to maintain physical affection for each other – cuddles, hugs, kisses, hair-stroking, massage, toe tickling, back rubbing, pet names, whispering endearments – these are all ways to express your feelings for each other without it necessarily leading to sex.

What to say to the children

If you have recently been diagnosed as ill, you may be wondering what to tell your children, especially if they are too young to understand everything that is going on. As a parent, you will naturally feel inclined to protect your children because you do not want them to worry or be afraid for you, yet at the same time you do not want to hide things from them.

In fact, children are much more resilient and philosophical than we often give them credit for. They can understand the most complex of situations if explained in a way they will understand or can relate to. Even the youngest children can take what adults think of as being 'bad news' in their stride.

What to do

- Tell them as matter-of-factly as you can.
- Try to find a simple way to explain what your illness is in a non-jargon way. You might be able to find an illustrated book about the body aimed at children that will help. Use this to point to the parts of the body you are referring to – or draw a picture.
- Explain how the illness makes you feel – that perhaps sometimes you feel tired, or grumpy, or not like playing.
- Make up a story about someone with an illness like yours. Your children may feel more comfortable asking questions or explaining their fears if the story is not overtly about you, so you can have the chance to allay their fears.
- Encourage your children to draw a picture about how they feel. Is the face sad or smiley? Ask them to explain what the picture means.

7

Asking for Help

When you are ill, it is not always easy to ask for help. For some, it is bad enough being ill, let alone having to admit that you cannot manage in some way. You may see having to ask for help as an admission that you are ill. This may sound silly – after all, if you know you are ill, what difference should it make? Yet somehow it can. For some, illness is a kind of defeat and no one likes to admit defeat. Yet there is no shame in sometimes admitting that you need help. You are not meant to be Superman or Superwoman! Everyone goes through times when they need a bit of a helping hand. What is more, finding a way to ask for help can give family and friends around you a role. Bear in mind they might feel helpless and might appreciate the chance to feel useful or to do something positive.

Getting the help you need without feeling a burden

Think about what you need. Do you need practical help? Someone to do a bit of shopping or occasionally cook a meal for you? Someone to help tidy up the house or cut the lawn? Maybe you need someone to write a letter for you or make a phone call on your behalf? Or drive you to a hospital appointment or stay with you after treatment? Alternatively, perhaps you need company from time to time – just someone to talk to?

If you are not naturally the kind of person who feels comfortable to ask others for favours or openly express your needs then to do so when you are not feeling your best or feeling more vulnerable than usual seems to be asking the impossible. You might think you should not need to ask – that others should instinctively know that at a time like this you need help. What is interesting is that others may feel at a loss to know what to do. They may realize you are independent and feel awkward about asking for help so they hold back, afraid of offending or hurting your feelings. Perhaps they do not want to presume you need help in case their offers of assistance are derided or rejected or they overstep the mark. In short, they could be terrified of doing or saying the wrong thing! So how can you bridge this impasse? How can you ask for the help you need without losing face? How can you communicate to others your needs without making them feel awkward?

What to do

- Remember that you cannot help being ill. It is not wrong to admit that you have vulnerabilities or there are certain things you are unable to do for yourself. So stop feeling guilty or ashamed.

- Asking for what you need does not impose your will or force others to do something they do not wish to do. The other person still has a choice as to whether or not to help as long as you ask for what you want in a clear, concise and straightforward way. Say, 'Would you be able to . . .' or 'Could you . . .' or 'I would like you to . . .', and then ask for what you want.

- Be prepared that if you ask for something, it may be refused. That does not mean the other person does not like or love you or is neglecting you. Accept their refusal with good grace.

- Avoid any hint of emotional blackmail in order to give the other person a genuine feeling of choice. For example, if you preface your request with a statement such as 'I have no one else to ask', you would clearly be piling on the pressure and make it difficult for the other person to say no. In some circumstances you may feel you have no alternative but to apply extra pressure in order to get the help you need, but at least be honest with yourself and with the other person so that you are both under no illusions.

How to make more time for you

One aspect of illness often underestimated is the sheer lack of time you now find for yourself. This is often in sharp contrast with the view of illness others may have. If you are off work others may consider you 'lucky' because you have no chores or responsibilities and lots more time to relax. Yet often the opposite is true. First, in itself, being ill takes up a lot of time and energy. Coping with symptoms, planning treatment, attending doctors' appointments, all take time. In addition you may have family and home responsibilities to fit in too – children to care for, a home to clean, a partner to cook for. You may already feel your illness is 'taking up' all your spare time, so that you feel guilty asking for more time to be alone or relax. Yet finding time for yourself is even more important when you are unwell. This is the time you need to recharge your batteries, to take stock, to reprioritize, to relax and replenish your energy levels, or just to do nothing for a change. But how can you make time for yourself when there are so many demands on your time?

What to do

- Do not try to be a perfectionist. Aim for 'good enough' rather than absolutely perfect.
- Stop procrastinating. It wastes time and piles on the stress.
- Do not spend time with people you do not like just because they have issued an invitation. Treat time as a valuable commodity – every moment you spend making small talk to someone you dislike is time you could have spent with your family or relaxing by yourself!
- Do not offer cups of tea or coffee to unexpected visitors if you feel you cannot spare time to talk to them.
- Do not put everyone else's needs before your own.

Part 3
Managing pain, stress and other symptoms

8
Managing Pain

Living with pain, day in, day out, is unbelievably wearing and disheartening. In theory, these days there is no reason why anyone should experience chronic pain. There are new wonder drugs and pain management techniques that do work. But they do not necessarily work every moment of every day for every person. And when pain is not relieved it can make you feel depressed and scared. It is also very hard for those around you to see you in pain and be unable to help. Those closest to you may love you so much that they feel they would rather be in pain themselves than see you suffer.

Pain is at best annoying and inconvenient, at worst it is very, very frightening and can severely limit what you can do. You owe it to yourself to get as much help as you possibly can.

What is pain?

So what exactly is pain? Pain is usually due to some kind of tissue damage and is the body's warning signal something is wrong. When you sustain an injury, electrical impulses or pain messages are transmitted from pain receptors along nerve pathways to the spinal cord and then to the brain. There are pain receptors all over the body and nerve impulses are relayed back from the brain to the site of the pain and surrounding muscles and organs. In some situations this helps keep you out of danger as it ensures you take appropriate action – removing your hand from a hot object, for example. Sometimes, however, pain starts for no obvious reason and the cause cannot be found.

Two main types of pain are of particular concern. Acute pain is the body's response to a particular injury or illness and usually possible to treat if it is relatively short-lived and responds to painkillers. Chronic pain, on the other hand, can continue on and off for years and is harder to relieve. One difficulty is that emotional and psychological factors can play a part in our perception of chronic pain. Often it is the unpredictability of pain that makes it hard to bear. This can lead to anxiety – wondering when the pain will come again and how bad it will be. It also makes it difficult to plan and lead a normal life. It is hard to accept invitations or even do normal things if you think you may be in pain.

Common sense tells us that if you feel tired or fed up you may feel pain more easily. Severe stress can also cause physical changes in the body that exacerbate pain. When you are stressed your muscles tense up which can increase the level of discomfort experienced. The more stressed you are, the fewer endorphins reach the brain – endorphins are the body's natural painkillers. So it follows that trying to relieve stress, through relaxation techniques, can directly help to relieve pain.

In addition, if you experience pain on a regular basis, your nervous system can become almost conditioned to expect pain and if muscles close to the area where you normally experience pain tense up for any reason, then the pain receptors may be activated with the result you feel discomfort. Again, your emotions play a part in that your previous experience of pain can also have an influence. If you have had a bad experience with, say, an injection, you will know that it can colour subsequent experiences, giving rise to anxiety and actually heightening your perception of pain. You may also experience what is known as 'referred' pain, where an injury or trauma at one site in the body is felt somewhere completely different. A familiar example is the way someone having a heart attack may feel pain in their arm.

Chronic pain that is not relieved is very debilitating and can result in poor sleep, feelings of depression and helplessness and decreased appetite. It can also result in a lower pain threshold so that a pain that seemed bearable before begins to seem unbearable.

Describing pain

It is very important to tell your doctor if you are in pain, exactly where the pain is, what it feels like, how long it lasts and whether or not anything you have tried gives relief. Describing pain can be quite difficult yet it can help your doctor understand precisely the cause which in turn will help him or her to treat it more accurately. There is absolutely no point in trying to ignore pain. It is your body's way of telling you something is wrong and trying to protect you from further damage, so it makes sense to try to find and deal with the cause. If you allow pain to take a grip, you can get into what is known as a 'vicious cycle' which is more difficult to treat, so it is important to remember that using pain relief is not a sign of weakness. It is essential to keep the pain under control.

It may help you to look at the following list of words, some of which were suggested by Ronald Melzack, one of the world's leading pain researchers at McGill University in Montreal, Canada, and see if any help describe your pain:

Aching	Pricking
Agonizing	Pulling
Annoying	Pulsing
Burning	Radiating
Cramping	Raging
Crushing	Relentless
Cutting	Searing
Dragging	Sharp
Dull	Shooting
Exhausting	Sore
Fleeting	Spreading
Frightening	Squeezing
Gnawing	Stabbing
Grinding	Stinging
Intense	Terrifying
Intermittent	Throbbing
Itchy	Tingling
Nagging	Tugging
Penetrating	Unbearable
Piercing	Vicious

Questions your doctor might ask you about your pain

- Where is it?
- When did it start?
- What does it feel like? (See list of words above)
- How severe is it? (It might be helpful to think in terms of a scale from 0 to 10. 0 means no pain, 10 means unbearable)

- How often does it occur? Every few minutes, every few hours, once a day, only at night?
- How long does it last? A few minutes at a time or for hours at a stretch?
- Does anything make the pain worse? For example, eating, drinking, sitting or lying in a certain position.
- Does anything make the pain better?
- What does your pain prevent you from doing? Does it stop you from doing normal activities – going out, doing household chores or even holding a conversation?
- What pain relief have you tried and did it help? Which ones did not help?

What to do about pain

- Talk to your doctor to see what can be done. Do not wait until the pain is very bad as it may be easier to control when the pain is mild.
- Describe the type of pain, how long it lasts, when it occurs and its intensity.
- If you are prescribed medication, follow your doctor's instructions carefully – if you do not understand, ask for a fuller explanation. For example you may be told that it is vital to take the medication at regular intervals even if the pain seems to be a bit better.
- If your pain gets worse or you find that the medication you have been prescribed does not fully control the pain, do not just put up with it, tell your doctor so he or she can try something else. For example it may be that two or more different painkillers can work safely in conjunction with each other.
- Do not forget to remind your doctor about other medications and supplements you are taking, so they can prescribe safely. This is important because some medicines may interfere with the efficacy of a painkiller or may not be safely used at the same time.
- Also remember to tell your doctor about any allergies you have.
- Ask your doctor if the medication you have been prescribed is likely to cause side-effects. It may be that some side-effects such as nausea can be controlled by other medication. Some side-effects only last a few hours and then your body adjusts, so the doctor's advice may be to see how you get on before further medication is prescribed.

- You may be asked to keep a pain diary so your doctor can monitor whether your pain is getting worse.
- Ask if you could be referred to a specialist pain clinic.

The best treatment for pain

There is no one single treatment for pain. What works for one person may not work for you. Your doctor may suggest a single painkiller or combination of drug therapies, but you may also want to look at alternative remedies. Relaxation can play an important part in the management of pain and some complementary therapies such as acupuncture have a good track record too.

It may also be worth reviewing your diet – migraines, arthritis, digestive disorders, depression and other health problems can all be exacerbated or relieved by certain foods, so changing what you eat could help. Much depends on getting to know the illness you are suffering from and discovering what works for you.

There are many treatments that can help relieve pain. You may also want to consider other therapies which help to prevent pain too, by helping to relieve stress and anxiety. Options include:

Painkillers

There are broadly two types of painkillers, non-narcotic drugs such as paracetamol, and non-steroidal anti-inflammatory drugs (NSAIDs) such as aspirin and ibuprofen, which can be bought over the counter without a prescription; and stronger narcotic drugs such as codeine and diamorphine which must be prescribed by a doctor. Different painkillers have different uses. For example, NSAIDs are useful in reducing inflammatory pain in the muscles and joints caused by arthritis, while diamorphine is more likely to be used to treat conditions where other painkillers have not proved effective.

Sometimes a combination of drugs can be used to treat pain, but your doctor will talk to you about this and decide which drugs can be used safely together. Many people are worried that if they are prescribed narcotic drugs such as diamorphine or morphine they will become addicted. If you are concerned, talk to your doctor, but if your pain is carefully managed and the dose strictly adhered to, the drugs are unlikely to become addictive.

Other pain relievers

- *TENS* (Transcutaneous Electric Nerve Stimulation). A technique where mild electric currents are applied to the skin by a small power pack connected to two electrodes. The impulses which cause a tingling sensation seem to relieve pain.

- *Acupuncture.* Fine needles are inserted into the skin at particular points on 'meridian' lines. It sounds painful but you are likely to only feel a mild tingling sensation. Again, this is a highly effective way of relieving pain in some people. For more information about acupuncture see page 71.
- *Nerve blocks.* For example, anaesthetic type drugs or long-acting steroids can be injected into or around a nerve to reduce pain in certain areas.
- *Physiotherapy.* Usually designed to help you get back to regular activity.
- *A variety of relaxation techniques* can also help, like visualization and meditation. For more details see page 73.
- *Chiropractic and osteopathy* can help relieve some types of pain.
- *Hypnotherapy.* The hypnotherapist will talk to you and suggest mental images that will enable you to gain control over the amount of pain you feel. It does not work for everyone but some people find it highly effective. You can even learn self-hypnosis techniques to try at home.
- It is also worth considering a range of complementary therapies such as *Reiki*, a kind of meditative healing therapy which involves a therapist laying his or her hands on or near you in particular positions.

Bear in mind that everyone is different. What works for one person may be less effective for someone else. But with trial and error you may find something that works well for you. One reason it is important to deal with pain is that feeling you are in control of your pain can actually lower your pain threshold.

Do not forget to ask if it is possible to refer you to a specialist pain clinic – and do ask other people about what has worked for them.

9

Coping with Other Symptoms

Dealing with tiredness

Feeling tired all the time is one of the most common problems when you are suffering from chronic or long-term illness. Every person's experience is unique. Some people find it incredibly difficult to get up in the morning, regardless of whether they have had a good or bad night's sleep; others feel tired throughout the day and need to rest regularly. You may need to go to bed early in the evening or find that, despite feeling tired, you cannot sleep even if you go to bed late. Once in bed, perhaps you drop off to sleep as soon as your head hits the pillow but then wake again shortly afterwards and toss and turn all night long. Perhaps you crave sleep, but simply cannot drop off because you are in pain or you are worrying. Or maybe you sleep reasonably well for a few hours, but wake in the small hours and cannot go back to sleep no matter how hard you try.

The problem with tiredness is that it can affect so much of what you can and cannot do. If your tiredness is an intrinsic part of your illness, as with ME or cancer, other people may find it difficult to understand what it is really like for you. A lot of people think they know what tiredness is but the debilitating, all-consuming tiredness that accompanies an illness like ME is very difficult to describe and almost impossible to understand unless you have experienced it firsthand.

Inevitably, some friends and family will try to empathize with you by telling you they know just how you feel, but often they have absolutely no idea of the depth of tiredness you are experiencing. It is easy to feel annoyed at platitudes such as, 'I feel tired too sometimes' or 'I know how you feel'. But ultimately you must console yourself with the fact that they cannot know how you feel because they are not you. You might even sometimes find yourself uncharitably wishing they *could* know how you feel! Well, that is understandable too.

But there is no point blaming them. They are probably doing their best to try to empathize and help you feel less alone with your illness. Explaining that their attempts to cheer you up are misguided may help, but equally may be misunderstood, so choose your words carefully!

The only way to cope with tiredness is to give in to it. Learning to listen to and trust your body is vital if you are to muster enough energy to cope with your illness so do what you can – and then rest. Fighting tiredness, refusing to give in to rest even when every fibre in your body is telling you to slow down, is not sensible. Trust your instincts and your body will tell you when the time is right to do a little more. Do not see this approach as 'giving up'. Giving in gracefully to tiredness is very different from giving up. In a sense you are making a bargain with your body. It is almost as if you are saying: 'You won't let me down if I do not push you too far.' There are no guarantees, of course. Your illness must take its course, but you can still feel in control. The way to see it is that you are *choosing* to listen to your body, *choosing* to rest, *choosing* not to overdo it.

One way to look at things is to see yourself as a manager of your illness. However scary and out of control your illness seems, in fact, on a day-to-day level, you are in control of more than at first seems apparent. You control what you think of your illness for a start, whether you view it as the worst thing that has ever happened to you or whether you can see some good things about it too. You control whether you have a positive attitude towards managing your illness, or whether you are going to simply give up and feel sorry for yourself. You control whether you listen to your body's needs and take a rest, or whether you push yourself to the limit and then have to cope with feeling even worse the next day. You control whether you take your medication or not or whether you do your best to find out about alternative therapies that might offer relief for certain symptoms or whether you choose not to. However bleak things seem, there is always some small step you can take for yourself. Looking at your diet, for example. (For more about diet, see page 90.) Making that extra effort will help you to feel better about yourself, boost your confidence, bolster your self-esteem and help you deal more effectively with the difficulties you face along the way.

Susan, 25, was recently diagnosed with Crohn's disease after nearly ten years of bowel problems and ill health: 'Once I knew what I was dealing with, I felt much stronger and able to fight it. I decided I wanted to find out as much as I could about the disease so I could find solutions that worked for me. It wasn't easy. I had already been backwards and forwards to doctors and hospitals and no one had really been able to help me and the drugs prescribed had not worked. But I was determined to help myself. I had already suspected that food played a role in the way I felt as I noticed that when I ate certain things such as high fibre or acidic foods, I had bouts of diarrhoea, vomiting and abdominal pain. I began to keep a detailed food diary so I could see for myself how different foods made me feel and as a result I was able to devise an eating plan that helps keep the worst of my symptoms at bay. And I am always receptive to new ideas about treatment – I'm thinking of looking into homeopathy next and I'm also learning about relaxation techniques. I still take a lot of medication and nutritional supplementary drinks but I feel I am now living with, not suffering from, Crohn's disease.'

How to get a good night's sleep

Not getting enough sleep or finding that your sleep pattern is disturbed can make you feel depressed, irritable and leave you lacking in energy. On top of other symptoms, it can be the last straw. Worrying that you are not getting enough sleep can make the problem worse so it becomes a vicious circle. Try the following:

- Only go to bed when you are tired.
- Get up at the same time each day, whether you are sleepy or not.
- If you wake during the night, do not lie there tossing and turning – get up and do something mundane or read until you feel sleepy again.
- If you wake very early, and no longer feel sleepy, it is best to get up rather than toss and turn for an extra couple of hours in bed.
- Avoid watching TV or reading anything too stimulating before you try to sleep.
- Make sure the bedroom is dark, quiet and well ventilated.
- Do not allow your bedroom to get too hot – below 70F (21C) is ideal.
- Avoid any kind of stimulants for at least an hour and a half before bedtime – that means tea, coffee, cocoa, cola drinks and alcohol.
- Do not smoke just before bedtime.
- Avoid taking a nap in the afternoon, unless it is really necessary.
- Avoid eating too late.
- Try having a milky drink last thing – but not if you already tend to have to get up to use the toilet.
- If you are able, take some exercise during the day – this will help tire you out physically.
- Try having a hot bath immediately before bedtime.

Nausea

Nausea is a common side-effect of certain drugs, but your doctor should be able to prescribe an anti-nausea preparation to combat this symptom. Look carefully at what you are eating to see if a small adjustment in your diet could help too. For example, it might be sensible to steer clear of highly spiced or very rich food.

Loss of appetite

A poor appetite is another common symptom associated with illness. It may be the direct result of an infection or various digestive disorders but it could be a side-effect of the medication you have been prescribed. In addition, appetite can be dramatically affected by how you feel 'in yourself'. If you feel anxious, stressed or worried, then your appetite may be disturbed, though this can vary from person to person. Some people tend to eat more when they are anxious (hence the phrase 'eating for comfort'), but others cannot face food. It is important to identify the cause of your loss of appetite – if your illness can be successfully treated, your appetite should improve. In the meantime, do what you can to tempt the palate. Eating little and often is a good idea – small portions of nutritious food at regular intervals.

Mood swings and irritability

Feeling fed up and being moody go hand in hand with illness. However well you are coping, there are bound to be days when you feel like this. The various symptoms you suffer from can all take a toll and impinge upon each other. If your appetite is poor, that can accentuate feelings of tiredness, which in turn can exacerbate depression and so on. The sheer drudgery of feeling ill all the time inevitably affects your mood. There are no easy answers. First, it is important to recognize that mood swings, irritability and depression are almost certainly a normal reaction to what you are going through. Having said that, it is definitely worthwhile talking to your doctor about how you feel. It may also be worthwhile talking to a counsellor on a regular basis to help you through a particularly bad patch.

On a day-to-day level there are other strategies you can adopt to help you through. It is a good idea to talk to your family and tell them how you feel, for example. Maybe there are days when you feel you would rather be left alone to 'stew' for a bit rather than constantly have people try to cheer you up! Explain this in advance so the family can steer clear of you and let you work through your emotions without additional pressure.

Another idea is to prepare a 'happy box'. The idea is to collect, over time, some favourite bits and pieces that make you happy and put them together in a drawer or box which you only open when you really need cheering up. The happy box might contain a favourite CD, some photographs of particularly happy times on holiday, some special mementos of a good time in your life, something that always makes you laugh, an inspirational poem and so on. You can add to the box at any time but only open the box when you really need it – see it almost as a lifeline when you experience your darkest moments.

Mood and diet

In addition you may consider looking at your diet. Diet is increasingly thought to play a key role in mood and depression, because different nutrients help regulate neurotransmitter activity. Neurotransmitters are chemicals which carry messages from one brain cell to another and affect how we feel and behave. Some neurotransmitters inhibit nerve function and help calm us down. Others stimulate nerve function and perk us up.

Antidepressant drugs are often designed to work by altering levels of particular neurotransmitters – such as raising levels of serotonin in the brain. If the brain is deprived of essential nutrients, then its function is impaired and our mood and emotions are affected. So, if you eat a carbohydrate-rich food such as pasta, brain concentrations of tryptophan, an amino acid which is the building block for a neurotransmitter called serotonin, are raised – increased serotonin helps relieve depression.

There is increasing research into the effect of food on our mood and behaviour. We already know, for example, that confusion, fatigue and memory loss may be related to a poor diet and several studies have shown that depressed people have low levels of the B vitamins.

So what nutrients should you aim to include in your diet to help lift your mood?

- *Niacin* Best sources: chicken, fish, pulses, brewer's yeast, wheat bran, peanuts, beef, and wholegrain wheat products and fortified cereals. Fruits, vegetables and dairy products all contain some niacin as do dates, figs and prunes. Milk and eggs are good sources of tryptophan which can convert to niacin in the body provided iron, vitamin B6 and riboflavin are present. You should be able to get sufficient niacin from your diet and excessive supplements can be dangerous.

- *Folic acid* Best sources: offal, yeast extract, green leafy vegetables and fortified breakfast cereals.
- *Vitamin B1 (thiamine)* Best sources: milk, offal, pork, eggs, vegetables and fruit, wholegrain cereals and fortified breakfast cereals. All white flour has to be fortified with thiamine in the UK.
- *Vitamin B2 (riboflavin)* Best sources: milk, dairy products, potatoes, fortified breakfast cereals, brown rice, and Marmite.
- *Vitamin B6* Best sources: widely present in foods especially in meat, fish, eggs, whole cereals and some vegetables including peas, and potatoes.
- *Vitamin B12* Best sources: only present in animal products and yeast. Liver is the best source but eggs, cheese, milk, meat, fish and fortified breakfast cereals all contain this vitamin.
- *Vitamin C* Best sources: most vegetables and fruit contain vitamin C, but storage and cooking can deplete it which is why it may be worth considering a supplement.
- *Magnesium* Best sources: vegetables, peanuts, Marmite, sardines, chicken, cheese.
- *Iron* Best sources: liver, sardines, fortified breakfast cereals, chocolate, red wine.
- *Selenium* Best sources: meat, fish and cereal products.
- *Tyrosine and phenylalanine (amino acids)* Best sources: turkey, chicken, chocolate and milk.
- *DHA (docosahexaenoic acid)* – otherwise known as omega-3 fish oil found in oily fish such as herrings, mackerel, tuna, salmon and sardines.

However, if you are considering taking a supplement of any kind you should discuss it first with your doctor.

Coping with mobility problems

Finding you are unable to move around as easily as you once did can be very distressing. If you have always been independent, you may find it hard to accept that your body no longer allows you to come and go as you please. You may be forced to rely on others for assistance to get in and out of a chair or bed, or up and down stairs, or in and out of a car. Or find that you walk more slowly, or are unsteady on your feet and have to hold on to something, or rest regularly for fear of falling.

It is very hard for those who have not been ill to fully appreciate the impact these changes and limitations can have on your life or how they can affect your morale, your very sense of self. Most of us take our mobility for granted – and that, in itself, makes it hard for others to really understand what you are going through.

The body is so complex and its parts so interdependent in ways we normally take for granted that even seemingly minor limitations can have dramatic consequences. If you have lost the use of an arm either through something as seemingly innocuous as a broken arm or as serious as a stroke, at first it can be almost impossible to get in and out of a bath unaided, for example. It sounds absurd but it is surprisingly difficult.

Coming to terms with loss of mobility can be as traumatic as coming to terms with becoming ill. Unlike many other aspects of your illness, it is hard to hide mobility problems. You can put on a brave face and hide the pain you are enduring, but it is impossible to hide the fact that you have difficulty walking. This may mean you are forced to rely on others for help – and if you have always valued your independence, as most of us do, this can be very hard to adjust to, and a constant reminder that you cannot do what you used to. In addition, your disability is there for others to see and they may jump to all sorts of conclusions about you that are wrong. Just because you have difficulty moving around, they may assume you have difficulty thinking sensibly or making decisions for yourself!

Pat, 52, has suffered from multiple sclerosis for 13 years. 'I am not the kind of person who bangs on about my illness. In general, I do not even mention it unless I really have to. What gives me away is the fact I wobble a bit when I walk and increasingly have to use a walking stick. I get so frustrated I could scream. I know what I want my body to do. I know where I want my legs to move. But they just won't do what I tell them to do. It is so maddening. I do not feel sorry for myself at all and think I am an upbeat person in general, but I rage against not being able to do what I want, when I want. I used to be quite sporty and fit, now I find it a struggle to stay active. I was never one for sitting around doing knitting! At first, I used to be able to hide my illness, not just from others, but from myself. When other people didn't know and couldn't guess just by looking at me – and I chose not to tell them – it was a kind of release. Now, people see me wobble and are more inclined to ask if I'm all right and so the questions start and I feel like public property. I want my illness to be private but my body gives me away.'

The sheer frustration of having to move slowly or carefully when you have mobility problems can take its toll on your morale and self-esteem. It can serve as a constant reminder of your illness when you might otherwise have been able to put it out of your mind for a while. It can also be very frightening. We all expect a certain loss of mobility as we grow older, but when it comes too soon, it inevitably resonates with our innermost fears about dying as well as our fears of being unable to care for ourselves and being dependent upon others. You may feel a sense of being out of control of your body, being afraid of if, how and when you might deteriorate further.

At times like this, your imagination can run riot – it is understandable, but counterproductive. It is easy to say try to take each day as it comes. Yet looking too far ahead, fearing constantly about what the future may hold is frightening and debilitating to the point where it can ruin the good days as well as the bad.

You may need to start mourning the loss of your mobility. Owning up to the fact you feel sad or angry about what you can no longer do is a key part of coming to terms with your situation. Talking about it with someone who knows what it is like could help a great deal – which is one reason why contacting a suitable self-help group might be beneficial. Try to look at your mobility difficulties, whatever they are, in terms of what you can do, rather than what you cannot. Again, it is easy to say, but it will help in the darkest hours when you can only despair at what you have lost. Try to find something positive to cling on to, however insignificant it may seem.

For some, your illness may mean that you have to adjust to using a wheelchair. The enormity of this transition cannot be underestimated. There are no easy platitudes to help you feel better. Certainly, the first days will undoubtedly be among the worst as you try to adapt to the new skills you will need to manoeuvre the chair. Not to mention adjusting to the countless ways it will undoubtedly affect your life, what you can do, where you can go and how others view and treat you. Again, talking to others who have been through the same experience may be invaluable.

Give yourself time to adjust – expect to feel frustrated, inept, angry, sad, or, confusingly, perhaps even some relief that you are finally chair-bound and no longer have to struggle to move around. It may mean the end of some problems, the fear of falling for example, but it is bound to be the start of others, such as difficult access to places you used to go to without a second thought.

A word about exercise

One problem about being less mobile is not keeping active or exercising. But there are plenty of exercises you can do to keep your circulation moving and even stay fit. Below are three simple exercises you can try – but the golden rule is to only do what you feel comfortably able to manage. If you feel dizzy or faint or tired, then use your common sense, and STOP.

Simple chi kung exercises

The Chinese exercises known as qigong or chi kung are very useful when you have limited mobility – this form of exercise is linked to t'ai chi. You have probably seen people doing t'ai chi on television – it is a very slow, gentle but deceptively powerful form of exercise. In China it is commonplace for whole communities to gather in the park in the early morning to practise their t'ai chi and chi kung before work.

The idea is to harness and increase energy, strengthen your resistance to disease and improve your circulation. Even if you do not believe in the Chinese idea of building up inner 'chi' or energy, you will find the three exercises below beneficial – they can all be done sitting down. If you have high blood pressure, or a bad back, check with your doctor first, just to be on the safe side.

Holding the ball

1 Sit in a comfortable chair, preferably an upright chair. Sit up as straight as you can. Start by 'gathering chi'. Place your right hand over your *dan tien* – a point just below your belly button considered to be your energy centre. Then place your left hand over your right hand. Your hands are close together but don't touch. You are now 'centring' yourself and 'gathering chi', ready to start. Take a moment to relax and focus on your breathing.

2 Bring your arms up and position them as though you are holding a very large balloon straight in front of you. Your arms will be relaxed and curved, fingers slightly apart, hands not touching. Close your eyes and breathe deeply and as slowly as you can. Breathe in and out about ten times or until you feel your arms start to ache. Imagine you are holding a ball of energy.

3 Now lower your arms and 'gather chi' at the *dan tien* position.

Resting on water
1 Sit comfortably as above and 'gather chi', ready to start.
2 Take your arms out to the sides and imagine that you are standing in a beautiful shallow lake, the water is up to your waist and your hands are out to either side of your body, resting on the water, almost as though to balance you. Spread your fingers so you can feel the water gently slipping through them. Keep your shoulders relaxed. Breathe in and out deeply and slowly for about ten times or for longer if you feel comfortable.
3 Now lower your arms and 'gather chi' at the *dan tien* position.

Breathe in healing energy
1 Sit comfortably as above and 'gather chi', ready to start.
2 Lower your hands so they rest on your lap, palms upturned, close to your body. Slowly bring your hands up to just under your chin. As you do this breathe in deeply and imagine you are breathing in lots of wonderful healing energy.
3 When your hands reach your chin, turn the palms outward and upward and continue the movement smoothly, breathing out, until the hands are high above your head, pushing away towards the sky. As you do this, imagine you are pushing away all the negative energy inside you, pushing all your fears and negative thoughts away.
4 Now reposition your hands, still high above your head, but so that the palms are parallel, facing each other, about 9 inches apart. As you breathe in, imagine you are a channel for positive energy and draw in that positive energy from the sky, sliding your hands, so they come down, either side of your head, and then come under your chin again, palms facing down.
5 Continuing the movement smoothly, breathe out as you push your hands away from your body in a slow, controlled but powerful movement, again, pushing all your negative energy and thoughts away.
6 Finally, breathe in, and gather positive chi as you bring your hands back to the *dan tien* position.

Other exercises to try
• Raise your arms up in front of your chest, elbows bent, clench fists and place knuckles together. Fling hands to sides, bending arms at the elbow, as though opening double doors, and then

bending at the elbow, bringing hands back in, knuckles to knuckles. Do this vigorously about 20 times or until you get bored!

- If you can manage to hold a weight – a baked bean can would do to start with – try holding a can in each hand, and doing a simple 'upward press'. Sit with your back straight and your head in line with your spine. Hold the weights so your arms are bent at the elbow, and you are holding the weights in front of you at roughly shoulder height – your palms should face outwards. Breathe in. As you breathe out, bend your elbows slightly and press the weights above your head, keeping your knuckles pointing at the ceiling. Pause then breathe in as you lower the weights to shoulder height. Repeat six times if you feel able. Aim to build up repetitions gradually. Obviously, do not attempt this exercise unless you can hold the can safely in case it drops on your head or toes!

- If you have to sit or lie down for long periods, it is very important to keep your circulation moving. If you can, remember to wiggle your toes, point and flex your feet and do ankle circles regularly (aim for ten times an hour).

Getting practical help

Do bear in mind that you may be able to get practical help to ease your mobility difficulties. Ask your doctor if you could benefit from being referred to a physiotherapist. Regular sessions may help to keep your joints supple and mobile and the physiotherapist will be able to help you find a way of carrying out everyday tasks, such as getting in and out of bed, in a way that will work with, rather than against, your mobility limitations.

Also check out if you might be entitled to any special equipment – whether it is a walking frame or a stair lift. In the UK, under the Chronically Sick and Disabled Persons Act 1970, your local authority's social services department is obliged to arrange for the provision of certain equipment for you to live as independently as possible as well as possible adaptations to your home if you are disabled. But you cannot state what you want and expect to get it, as the local authority will ultimately decide what you are entitled to. You may need items to help with everyday living, such as handrails next to the bath and toilet, or the provision of a bathroom on the ground floor if you can no longer manage stairs. Health care equipment such as walking aids or a commode are more likely to be supplied by the NHS. Wheelchairs are provided and maintained free of charge under the NHS to anyone who needs one permanently. Your doctor should refer you to your local wheelchair service centre for assessment.

Some items may be easier to get hold of than others – and many items are likely to be 'loaned' to you rather than bought for you specially. To find out more, ask your doctor for advice or contact your district nurse, health visitor, physiotherapist or social services department for advice.

If you are considering buying something for your personal use, see if you can arrange a no obligation, free trial first, especially in the case of more expensive or larger items, in case it turns out you need something different, or they are not much use after all.

For general advice about equipment, contact the Disabled Living Foundation (see Resources). You may find that there is a Disabled Living Centre in your area where you can see a range of equipment on show, try it out and get free advice.

10

Reducing Stress

When the body is under stress, the brain activates the Autonomic Nervous System in a bid to help us cope – the 'fight or flight' mechanism needed by early man in order to run away from, or fight, danger. For example, adrenaline stimulates the delivery of oxygen to the brain and muscles, preparing them for action by increasing the heart and breathing rate – handy if you are faced with a charging bull because the additional adrenaline would help you run faster. And the adrenal glands are stimulated to release a hormone called cortisol which raises blood pressure. But if adrenaline and cortisol are released and not 'used up' then unpleasant symptoms result – the classic signs of stress. Typical symptoms of stress include chest pains, diarrhoea, tiredness, changes to your appetite, dry mouth, inability to concentrate, poor memory, palpitations and reduced sex drive.

Of course, if you are in a genuine 'fight or flight' situation, the body is primed for action in a way that will help you survive. But all too often the autonomic nervous system is triggered in inappropriate situations – if you get upset at work, stuck in a traffic jam or supermarket queue, cannot manage your child's tantrum, find it difficult to juggle all your responsibilities, or you are worried about being ill. And that is when stress becomes less than helpful. In effect your body is being primed for action, but remains sedentary.

Unfortunately, it is thought that if you regularly subject your body to this kind of stress, the adrenaline and cortisol released depress the immune system, making you more susceptible to infections and generally feeling run down. If adrenaline and cortisol are secreted into the bloodstream in large amounts, they cause fatty acids to be released into the blood from stores in the body. Persistent elevation of fatty acid levels in the blood impair the circulation and may in the long run put extra strain on the heart, increasing your risk of a heart attack.

Of course, sometimes stress can be good for you – if you are facing a job interview, or taking an exam, then the extra adrenaline pumped around the body can give you a boost just when you need it. But unfortunately, today's lifestyles often mean some of us feel stressed all the time, while illness itself can be a source of stress. We have already mentioned some of the difficult emotions it can unleash and all the difficulties you may face when dealing with family and friends or the medical profession as well as possible problems with self-image and self-esteem. These can all take their toll from a stress point of view. Indeed, many alternative practitioners see illness as being directly linked to stress. Disease is seen as being literally at dis-ease with your body, a body out of balance and under siege or stressed in the broadest sense.

So what can you do about stress? The good news is that you can learn stress-reducing and relaxation techniques which actually help reduce your heart rate and lower high blood pressure. The key is to learn to manage stress more effectively. If you can view problems more optimistically and take positive action to adapt to a problem or manage it differently or mitigate the more unpleasant effects by, say, relaxation techniques, you will decrease the amount of stress you feel and be healthier as a result.

How to relieve stress

- *Regularly create some peace and quiet for yourself.* Go for a walk, read a book, listen to some calming music.
- *Take some deep breaths.* Breathe in through your nostrils, hold it for a second and breathe out slowly through your mouth.
- *Visualize a calming scene* – lying on a beach, floating on air, walking by a stream on a spring day, etc. Use an image you find peaceful.
- *Have a good stretch.* Raise your arms and feel the stretch in your body from your finger tips to your toes.
- *If you can, take some exercise.* This will make you feel more positive about yourself as well as providing an outlet for any angry feelings you have. Regular exercise also triggers the body's endorphin system – circulating 'feel good' hormones and improving your mood. Even if you cannot move around very easily, there are exercises you can do sitting down. (See p. 53 for some examples.)
- *Do not let problems build up.* Find someone to talk to about how you feel.
- *Try to develop a positive attitude.* You will cope with stress less well if you are negative about everything. (See page 20 for ideas.)
- *Develop realistic expectations.* If you try to fit too much into your life or expect more from people than they can give, you will constantly be disappointed. Go with the flow, be pleased when

things go well, more laid back when things do not go according to plan.

- *Consider having a pet*. Research shows that people who have pets need to see their doctors less and report fewer minor ailments. An Australian study shows that blood pressure and cholesterol levels of pet owners were significantly lower than those who didn't have a pet.
- *Make some new friends*. This may sound silly but there is evidence to suggest that if you have a network of social relationships you are likely to cope better with stress.
- *Treat yourself to a regular massage if it is at all possible* – touch is a powerful de-stressor.
- *Allow yourself a 'worry ten minutes' every day if necessary*. Tell yourself you can worry all you like in that period but then switch off completely. This is a way of helping you to contain the worries rather than allowing them to spill over into every area of your life.
- *Eat a good quality diet* with plenty of fresh fruit and vegetables.
- *Get into a good sleep routine.*
- *Have more fun!*

11

The Mind–Body Connection

It seems incredible that some people are still resistant to the idea that the mind – our emotions, what we think and feel – can directly affect our health, as though somehow the mind is a completely separate entity, and immune to all the stresses and strains we put ourselves under. We take it for granted that an illness can be highly complex and that it can affect the body in many different ways. After all, the body is an extraordinarily complex living system – every individual part is complex in itself yet a part of the whole and interrelated with every other part. So it is hardly surprising that the mind and the emotions are inextricably linked too.

Is illness all in the mind?

Yet there is an extraordinary unease and stigma attached to the idea of the mind somehow being implicated in illness. To be told that an illness is 'all in your mind', 'psychological' or 'psychosomatic' is seen as a most terrible affront, a damning accusation that must be contradicted and defended at all costs. If someone says your illness is 'all the mind' you might feel they do not believe that you have the symptoms you say you have, that you are imagining them or that you are exaggerating their severity. You might even feel they are saying you are mentally ill or mad or that the illness itself is a made-up one, that it does not exist at all.

In the past some illnesses, bronchial asthma and ulcerative colitis for example, were labelled as 'psychosomatic' because it was known they could be triggered by emotions such as anxiety. This led some medical practitioners to not view them seriously because for a long time psychological causes were not treated with the same seriousness or respect as physical causes. Many have wrongly come to think of the term 'psychosomatic' as indicating that a person has some kind of personality flaw. Of course, the symptoms are equally as serious and still need treatment – but somehow the fact that there is an emotional component has led to much stigma and misunderstanding.

Some medical practitioners have done untold damage in this area by declaring that some illnesses, such as Chronic Fatigue Syndrome,

Repetitive Strain Injury or Gulf War Syndrome are 'all in the mind'. And, indeed, it does seem some have intended their theories and remarks to mean that the sufferers are exaggerating or imagining their symptoms or even that the illness does not exist. It is bad enough when friends and family hint at such beliefs, but it seems sheer treachery when the medical profession itself makes such pronouncements. In many cases it seems they are not trying to deliver a helpful message about the genuine relationship between mind and body, but are creating a climate where sufferers are not believed and run the risk of being marginalized by both the medical profession and friends and family who are looking for an excuse not to understand the illness.

Fortunately, it is only a small percentage of the medical profession who hold such views, but they wield an inordinate amount of power because their pronouncements inevitably make good headlines in newspapers.

The great sadness is that these views tend to stifle genuine debate and better understanding of the undoubted link between mind and body. There is a world of difference between saying an illness is 'all in the mind' and acknowledging that emotions and attitudes can influence our state of health for better or worse. The fact that a few misguided people 'write off' certain illnesses or symptoms in a derogatory way makes it much more difficult for sufferers to openly look at the issues. It is as though if we dare allow a chink in the armour and let anyone see that we acknowledge there is a mind–body connection, somehow we are admitting that the doctors who say 'it is all in the mind' are right or have a point. The temptation is to therefore reject and avoid all debate on the subject rather than risk open discussion.

Yet for those who suffer from long-term illness, looking at the mind–body connection can be a valuable step in understanding their illness or learning to live with it. In some cases it can offer precise insights into why the illness occurred and how it might be controlled better or even cured.

Why do some of the medical professional hold these views? It can be helpful to bear in mind that doctors in training spend most of their time studying the nuts and bolts of illness and disease – they spend very little time thinking about health and well-being. They are trained largely to focus on making a diagnosis and prescribing medication from the information you can tell them about the physical symptoms you have. They do not usually ask you what state your emotions or relationships are in, whether you enjoy your job or how stressed you are! Apart from anything else, doctors are busy – focusing on physical symptoms is quicker than trying to find out why you might have the symptoms in the first place.

East meets West – the holistic approach

In the West we are used to thinking of the body as completely separate from the mind. The body tends to be viewed almost as a machine which, when it breaks down, has to be fixed. Doctors look to see how the part that has broken down can be fixed and so medicine is rather mechanistic and revolves around treating illness and symptoms rather than promoting health.

But the story is very different in the East where practitioners routinely treat people 'holistically' – that is they do not look at body parts in isolation but how the mind, body and 'spirit' work together. In Chinese medicine different emotions are even linked to particular organs and it is accepted that if you are unhappy or emotionally troubled it can have a knock-on effect somewhere in the body, presenting as a physical symptom.

A more commonplace example that we all take for granted is how sometimes we know that we have caught a cold because we are feeling 'run down'. We know instinctively that if we had been fighting fit, perhaps we would have escaped infection. The holistic approach is all that and more.

Even in the West, 2000 years ago the 'father of medicine', the Greek physician Hippocrates, was interested in the idea of the body's ability to heal itself and the importance of the relationship between mind and body. Today, although some doctors are still sceptical about such ideas, there is a new branch of science known as PNI – psychoneuroimmunology – which is gaining recognition and credibility. For example, there is currently quite a lot of research looking into how stress affects the immune system. Sceptics say that if someone succumbs to, say, a bacterial or viral infection, then it is the bug that causes the illness, not the state of mind of the person who is infected. On the other hand, lots of people can be exposed to the same bug but not everyone succumbs to the illness. Psychoneuro-immunologists are interested in why one person is more vulnerable than someone else. Could it partly be due to the fact that their immune system has been undermined because of stress? Also why do some HIV-positive patients live for 20 years or more while others die much sooner? Science has not yet provided an adequate explanation – but looking at how the mind and body work together might provide more clues.

Responsibility, not blame

One of the most attractive aspects of the holistic approach is that *you* are seen as the best expert on your own health and well-being. Many of the choices you make – how well you look after yourself, what you eat, the stress you subject your body to, how fit you keep, how well you manage your relationships, whether you get a balance between work and relaxation – play a crucial part in how healthy you are. In many ways, this is common sense. If you constantly ate junk food, never ate fruit and vegetables, rarely took any exercise, drank too much alcohol, bottled up anger and insisted on working 20 hours a day in an asbestos factory, you probably would not be too surprised if, in the end, you succumbed to illness! But the body, mind and spirit are also susceptible to much more subtle stresses and strains too. We may not be so well 'tuned in' to these subtleties, but at the very least it is reasonable to assume that the more we nurture ourselves, the greater our potential to be healthy.

The one difficulty about the holistic approach is that if you take the view that you are responsible for your health, while that is fine when you are healthy, it can seem as though you are being blamed when you get ill. This may be acceptable if you know you have over-indulged and done all the wrong things throughout your life, but what if you feel you have made reasonably healthy choices? Some people have misunderstood the holistic approach altogether. It is not its aim to apportion blame but to help us understand ourselves better and get in touch with what some holistic practitioners call our 'inner voice' – the part of us that knows what is best for us. That does not necessarily mean that by changing our eating habits or taking more exercise or finding more time to relax we will be able to cure our illness (though some might argue it is possible). But being open-minded about these ideas at the very least may help you to manage some of your symptoms better.

What if you feel you have tried everything but you are still experiencing a myriad of symptoms? There is no point in blaming yourself for your illness – that will not achieve anything. Remember that ill health can also be caused by environmental and other factors. You may have done everything right and still become ill. The important point is that no one wants to be ill. You did not get ill on purpose. Very few of us are saints who can consistently make all the right choices in our lives – sometimes we do make mistakes or over-indulge or become stressed despite our absolute best efforts. But that does not mean you cannot start thinking about your health in a holistic way from now on. Start listening to your 'inner voice' as of now. When your body tells you that you are overdoing it, stop. When you feel you cannot take on any more commitments, learn to say no. If you know you should make time to relax, then do not put it off. If you feel you have spent a lifetime caring for others, consider that now, maybe it is time for you.

Is a negative attitude about your illness holding you back?

If you are finding it difficult to be positive and inwardly feel aware that your illness dominates your life and the lives of most of those who are close to you, then it may be worth looking at why this is. Of course, if you are constantly in pain or so seriously ill that your prognosis is very poor, if you are bed-bound or suffering from symptoms that stop you from leading anything like a normal life, it is not surprising if you have little energy left over to think of other things. But there is a school of thought that might at least be worth a look. It can make uncomfortable reading, but if you are willing to suspend your disbelief for a moment and be open-minded, it may strike a chord and you may find it has something useful to say to you. If not, then simply discard it.

So what is it all about? The idea is simply that sometimes a negative attitude is difficult to shift because it is too 'useful'. How can a negative attitude be useful? There are many possible answers. The important thing to remember is that no one is judging you. If you recognize that one or more of the following is true for you and want to do something about it, then fine. If none strikes a chord, then that is fine too.

Six uncomfortable reasons why you can get stuck with a negative attitude

1 It is quite a good way of getting attention. If you are always negative, then chances are people who are positive will try to cheer you up!
2 It is easier. If you are positive, then it means you have to try to actively solve problems. It may seem tempting just to accept the status quo instead.

3 It is a way of avoiding responsibility if things do not turn out well. After all, if you are a positive person and try this or that in a bid to ease symptoms or attempt to beat your illness and it does not work, then you might feel it was your fault it failed.

4 You do not have anything to live up to. If you are a positive person, then everyone might expect you to get better. If you are a negative person, people are less likely to expect improvement.

5 At least you are prepared for the worst!

6 It may help you 'stay stuck' in the illness, which, in turn, may be resolving a problem. A simple example is that if you are ill, it might give you a cast-iron reason to avoid going out, helping others or getting a job. The difficulty is that you may not be aware of all this consciously and it can be hard to fathom out the underlying connections. It may be something to do with fear of responsibility, fear of showing your emotions, fear of failure or fear of rejection. Another way to approach this is to write a list of all the things you *would* be able to do if you were well. Do any of the things on that list make you feel uncomfortable? Ask yourself what would happen if your illness suddenly stopped. What disadvantages would there be?

It takes courage to consider these ideas and it may be completely irrelevant in your case but if any of this strikes a chord, you may want to talk about it in more detail with someone who is trained to listen – a counsellor, for example.

It can sometimes be useful to look back at what illness has meant to you or to other members of your family in the past. Try writing down your memories of ill health within the family – who was ill and when, how they reacted, how others responded, the things that were said within the family, what messages you learnt about what it was to be ill. Look at how people who were ill in your family (or you) were treated – were they shown sympathy or treated as a nuisance? Were they believed or treated with contempt or was it something no one liked talking about? What did illness stop them (or you) from doing? Were there any benefits to being ill or was it all bad? Sometimes major events in our childhood can leave a legacy that we are not really aware of or do not understand for many years. What are the feelings you remember you had about illness as a child? Fear? Excitement? Sadness? Anger? Guilt?

It is also worth thinking about the 'role' illness gives you – and other members of the family. Some people feel more comfortable in a caring role while others prefer being cared for. Sometimes being in one or other of these roles gives a person a good reason to put to one side issues they might not want to think about – a bad relationship, for example. And the thought of changing roles or changing the balance of a relationship can seem too scary as it is feared both parties have become used to their role – making a sudden change might even mean the end of the relationship itself. Again, if thinking about these things makes you feel uncomfortable or raises worries or unexplained feelings it may be helpful to consider talking them through with a counsellor.

Can positive thinking help?

Can positive thinking play a part in helping you deal with your illness? Could it even help you overcome your illness? There are always critics and sceptics who are keen to point out that it is almost impossible to set up reliable clinical trials to prove that positive thinking 'works'. But there is a compelling body of anecdotal evidence to suggest that it does play an important part for many people and really can make a difference.

Even if adopting a positive attitude does not influence the outcome of your disease, it can play an enormously important role in helping you to cope on a day-to-day level. There is already some evidence to show that thinking very negatively may adversely affect your immune system or stress hormones which could have a negative knock-on effect on health. And, certainly, if you feel negative about everything you may be less motivated to look after yourself. So it seems logical to suppose that trying to be positive could help boost your immune system, keep stress at bay and help you stay motivated to look after yourself and enjoy life to the full.

My own feeling is that it is sometimes hard to think positively if you are still at the stage where you feel your illness has not been sufficiently acknowledged or understood or appreciated by others. It can sometimes leave you 'stuck' in a place where you want to feel sorry for yourself for a while. It is almost as though until your illness has been fully accepted by others you can't move on. So if you can, try to talk to someone about your illness and what it is like for you. That doesn't mean you have to see illness as the 'enemy', but you can at least start to fight back.

Even if you have been given a gloomy prognosis by your doctor, there is no reason why you should not decide to adopt a positive attitude. There are people who have gone on to live much longer than anyone in the medical profession could have predicted. After all, the medical profession can be wrong. But even if in the end you don't live longer, a positive attitude really can help make what time you have more bearable. No one knows when they are going to die. You can spend every day worrying and fretting about it – or you can get on with the business of living. Having a positive attitude helps you do just that.

Richard, 56, was diagnosed in 1992 with multiple myeloma, a form of leukaemia: 'The diagnosis was a great shock to me and my family. I had felt unusually tired for a few weeks and felt something wasn't quite right despite the fact I was eating well and looked OK. When I saw a specialist and heard the diagnosis I must admit I was scared. You think of leukaemia and think you are going to die. In fact although there are new treatments available for many forms of leukaemia there is no cure for multiple myeloma so that was a big shock. Then, when I heard about the treatment regime I must admit I was scared but you just have to get on with it. There's no good feeling sorry for yourself. I had chemotherapy for three days every two weeks for six months. As soon as the chemo was over I would have zero strength and no energy – it would be even very difficult to get out of bed. That would last nine days and then I would have about two days when I felt well before the whole thing started over again.

Then I was referred to the marvellous Royal Marsden Hospital in London where I was given a stem cell transplant. That's a type of bone marrow transplant where your own blood is used to regenerate new bone marrow, followed by high-dose chemotherapy which completely wipes out your immune system. Since then I have been having special injections three times a week to kill off any cancer cells and slow the rate of their growth.

Yes, it has all been gruelling, but the treatment may put me into remission for about three years. If the disease comes back then I may be able to have the same treatment all over again. But I try not to think too far ahead.

I do believe positive thinking has helped me through. I know research is being done all the time and although all the people I know who have had this particular disease have now died – we've been to 13 funerals in the past few years – and I feel I am the only one left, I am still determined to make the most of every day. After all, that is what we should all do anyway. It makes me appreciate my wonderful wife and three fantastic sons even more. We no longer worry about the insignificant things in life – we're too busy living.'

What to do

- Remember that medical advances are being made all the time, new drugs are becoming available, new techniques discussed. Sometimes even doctors make mistakes. It is wrong to give anyone false hope but things may not be as bleak as you first thought. Keeping in touch with other sufferers and joining a relevant self-help group is one way to keep tabs on latest developments and find out what works for other people.
- Concentrate on improving aspects of your life that you can change – rather than dwelling on what you cannot. Even making tiny changes can help build up a sense that you are regaining control of your life and doing something positive for yourself.
- Do not feel guilty if you do not feel positive. It is hard to be cheerful all the time. Feeling negative is unlikely to drastically affect the ultimate outcome of your illness. So feel positive when you can, but do not worry if you cannot.

12

Could Complementary Medicine Help You?

There are literally hundreds of complementary or alternative therapies, ranging from those now considered to be mainstream such as homeopathy, acupuncture and chiropractic to the more alternative healing therapies such as Reiki. Not all doctors are sympathetic to complementary therapies – some are even suspicious of the most mainstream. Yet many people find them highly beneficial so it pays to be open-minded.

It is perhaps easy to see why the medical profession has been slow to accept complementary medicine. Most of what doctors are taught in medical school is based on scientific research and clinical trials – evidence-based medicine – so understandably they are more likely to question the anecdotal reports associated with complementary therapies, however powerful they are. Another factor is money. The medical profession and research into disease and cures largely revolves around the big bucks of the pharmaceutical industry. It is more difficult to gain funding into the benefits of, say, massage, because no one stands to make money out of the sale of drugs. Having said that, some doctors are more than enthusiastic about complementary therapies, they even have a therapist of one kind or another attached to their practice. A few are actually trained in and practise one or more therapies themselves.

The most commonly accepted complementary therapies within mainstream healthcare in the UK include osteopathy, chiropractic, acupuncture and homeopathy. Aromatherapy, reflexology and massage are also relatively widespread. But why would you want to consider a complementary therapy at all? Some people turn to alternatives because they feel orthodox medicine has failed them. Others are happy with the traditional treatment they have been receiving but worried about the effects of taking medication long term and are anxious to see if there might be an alternative strategy. Some people may have been recommended a therapy or have heard that it is especially good for combating a particular symptom they are suffering from. Others are interested in the holistic angle and the way most complementary therapies do not just treat a symptom or illness but look at the whole person – mind, body and spirit.

One attraction of many of the therapies on offer is that you are likely to get significantly more time with the practitioner than you would with a conventional doctor. An initial appointment with a homeopath can last anything up to an hour and a half. The therapist looks beyond your basic symptoms and in detail at many aspects of your health and well-being, likes, dislikes, past illnesses, even your personality traits to devise a treatment that works for you as an individual. It is this sense of personal attention that can seem very attractive if up to now you have always had to make do with a rushed few minutes with your doctor, only too aware that there is a long queue of impatient people back in the waiting-room.

A holistic approach

So what are the ideas underpinning a holistic view of health? The main premise is that it is no good just treating a symptom in isolation. For years, it has been almost a joke that hospital doctors and nurses used to refer to their patients not by name but by the disease they have – the 'liver' in bed 14 or the 'gall-bladder' in bed 10. But the body is not just a physical entity, a jumble of cells which work independently. It is a highly complex structure incorporating the mind and the emotions too. Ultimately, the aim in holistic medicine is to treat not just the symptom, but the whole person.

Many of the therapies focus on the idea of 'balance' and 'energy'. Here, the idea is that there is a state of natural balance within the body. When this balance is disturbed, perhaps because of environmental stress such as pollution or emotional stress such as bereavement, an imbalance in life energy can result which in turn may make us more susceptible to illness.

These ideas about health may be relatively new in the West, but in the East – China, for example – they have been an integral part of medicine for thousands of years. The Chinese refer to the opposite forces of yin and yang. Yin is cold and represents our feminine, soft and quiet side, while yang is warm and represents our masculine, strong and energetic side. When these two forces are in balance, good health results and the aim of Chinese medicine is to balance yin and yang so that the body's life-force or energy, called 'chi', can flow smoothly, enabling the body effectively to heal itself.

Many complementary therapies are based around the principle of energy, balancing the body's ability to heal itself, but each aim to manipulate the body's energy flow in its own way. An acupuncturist, for example, uses needles to stimulate particular points on one or more 'meridians' or invisible channels of the body. Energy is thought to flow along these channels to and from the various organs, maintaining physical, emotional and mental well-being. If the flow of chi is disrupted, or chi becomes blocked, perhaps because of an emotional upset, illness can result and the aim of acupuncture is to stimulate the flow of chi again to create greater harmony and balance within the body and kickstart the body's own healing mechanism.

Even if you think that the yin/yang or chi idea seems far-fetched, there is no disputing that acupuncture works. It can be a very effective way of blocking pain or lowering blood pressure and is frequently used to treat a whole range of conditions from migraines to addictions. Western medicine has attempted some explanation as to why acupuncture works – it causes the release of chemicals known as neurotransmitters which in turn carry messages to the brain. But acupuncture has so many uses and beneficial effects that it cannot easily be explained in Western terms by one neat theory – which is why the holistic Chinese version, though mysterious, is so attractive. But you do not necessarily have to understand *why* a particular therapy works or believe in any particular explanation for it to be of benefit. It is a question of seeing if it works for you.

Complementary therapies you may find useful

Acupuncture

Acupuncture is an increasingly popular ancient Chinese therapy, widely used in mainstream Chinese medicine. Needles are inserted into the skin at special points which lie along energy meridians. Each meridian is said to be linked to a main organ and by stimulating the acupuncture points, the practitioner aims to restore balance in the body. In traditional Chinese medicine the idea of yin and yang is important – the main meridians are either yin (dark, feminine, cold) or yang (light, male, warm) and an acupuncturist tries to rebalance yin and yang. The procedure does not usually hurt, but you might feel a tingling or numbness. Acupuncture is said to help with a wide variety of conditions including asthma, anxiety, stress, arthritis, circulation and digestive problems, though it does not work for everyone. It is a particularly effective form of pain relief.

Aromatherapy

Aromatherapy is the use of aromatic essential oils extracted from a wide variety of plants. Each oil is said to have unique properties which can be used to relax, soothe, energize or rebalance the body while others are noted for their healing abilities – anti-inflammatories, antiseptics or pain-relievers. The oils are very concentrated – it takes several kilos of lavender to produce a very small bottle of essential oil – and they can be used in different ways – massage, in the bath, or as an inhalation (smells can have a direct effect on our mood), but are most beneficial when rubbed into the skin. When used for massage, oils must be mixed with a 'base' or carrier oil, such as sweet almond oil, otherwise they can cause skin complaints. You must consult a qualified aromatherapist before using any oils on babies, children or if you think you might be pregnant as some oils can be dangerous if used inappropriately. Aromatherapy is particularly helpful in treating stress, insomnia, sinusitis, skin complaints and headaches.

Chiropractic

Practitioners use manipulation of the spine and joints to work on a variety of disorders associated with the musculo-skeletal system. A chiropractor may use X-rays to help him or her accurately diagnose where adjustment is needed and this is achieved by various 'thrust' techniques, such as applying sudden pressure to individual vertebra. Many people mistakenly think chiropractors deal primarily with back problems but in fact they can help a range of disorders including headaches, trapped nerves and asthma. McTimoney Chiropractic is a gentler form of the therapy. It is not uncommon for clients to experience a dramatic improvement after a single session.

Homeopathy

The basic idea is to try to stimulate the body's own healing potential by trying to 'cure like with like'. A minute, diluted dose of a substance is administered which in a larger dose, in a well person, would mimic the symptoms of the disease the practitioner is aiming to cure. Homeopathy is very much a holistic treatment, taking into account mind, body and spirit and your individual characteristics.

Hypnotherapy

Hypnotherapy works on the subconscious to change thoughts and behaviour, and can be very effective, particularly to combat pain. The therapist talks to you and induces a hypnotic state during which your breathing and heart rate will slow down. You will feel relaxed and may appear to be asleep but you will be aware of everything that is going on. You can even learn self-hypnosis.

Massage

Massage forms the basis of many therapies such as aromatherapy, but is of enormous value in its own right. A simple, relaxing massage can float away tensions, help boost circulation and stimulate the body's lymphatic system which is responsible for detoxifying the body. Massage is well worth considering if you are not involved in a relationship – the power of touch can be very beneficial and therapeutic.

Meditation

Many people say that regular meditation is a good de-stressor. You can pay to learn specific techniques such as Transcendental Meditation or have a go at home using very simple techniques anyone can try. Set aside about 15 to 20 minutes, sit quietly and notice your breathing and the rise and fall of your stomach as you breathe. If it helps, focus on a candle flame or repeat a made-up word, sometimes called a 'mantra'. At first your mind will wander, but gently refocus each time. Your breathing will gradually become more relaxed and deeper. If you find yourself sighing, it is a good sign and shows you are relaxing and breathing correctly.

Visualization

This is a kind of meditation and involves visualizing a relaxing scene – walking by a stream or lying in a meadow for example. Some people believe it is beneficial to visualize their body being enveloped by a healing white light and there are many visualization exercises you can try either on your own or in a group.

How to find a therapist

If you are interested in trying one or more complementary therapies, discuss it with your doctor. In the UK you can, in some cases, be referred under the NHS but provision is patchy – if not, you will have to book a private consultation.

There are around 45,000 complementary practitioners in the UK but unfortunately there is no one single register or code of practice. Some therapies have more than one governing or regulatory body which can make choosing a therapist quite difficult. The best approach is to find out as much as you can about the training the therapist has undergone, how much experience they have and what code of practice they abide by. If a therapist is unwilling or uncomfortable about answering questions about their training or experience, go to someone else. It is also sensible to choose a practitioner you like and get on with.

Charges vary from practitioner to practitioner and some offer a sliding scale according to how much you can afford but you might expect to pay anything from £15 to £50 a session. Sometimes a first consultation is free. Other therapists charge more for a first session because it usually takes longer especially if a full medical history is taken, but follow-up sessions may be less expensive.

When choosing a therapist, ask:

- about their training and experience;
- about the code of practice they abide by;
- if they have professional indemnity insurance;
- if they know about your particular health condition;
- how many sessions you are likely to need;
- how much treatment will cost.

During a first session, a therapist should:

- ask about your medical history;
- explain what the treatment involves;
- tell you what you can expect from the treatment;
- give you a chance to ask questions.

Avoid any therapist who tries to make a diagnosis or who guarantees that their treatment will cure your condition. You should consider complementary therapy as just that – complementary. Do not, under any circumstances, give up taking prescribed medication or abandon conventional treatment without first discussing it fully with your doctor.

You can get further advice from the Foundation for Integrated Medicine, the Institute for Complementary Medicine or the British Complementary Medicine Association (see Resources).

Part 4
Practical issues

13
Getting on With Your Doctor

Finding a doctor you like and trust is vital. Do you want someone who knows about the illness you are suffering from – or who is at least willing to find out more about it? Someone who is sympathetic and compassionate? Someone who will listen to what you want to say about your symptoms and your views on the side-effects of medication or ideas on treatment options? Do you want someone who believes that you are ill and does not make you feel stupid or awkward or that you are exaggerating or complaining unnecessarily? Someone who treats you as an equal rather than a child? Someone who respects your vulnerability without putting you down or acting in a superior manner? Someone who does not rush through consultations and who is receptive to new ideas or theories?

Not surprisingly, it adds up to a tall order especially in a climate where doctors are under immense pressure. Finding one who can meet all your needs and who is sympathetic, friendly, charming and has all these other qualities may not be easy. What if your doctor is old-fashioned and authoritarian? What if you sense they do not believe you or think you are exaggerating? What if they are not interested in your theories or ideas and they are not sympathetic? What if you dread going to the doctor or come away feeling let down or even upset because you feel misunderstood or not really listened to?

You could think about changing your doctor, but that is not always easy, depending on where you live. If you have had the same family doctor for many years, you may feel unable to ask for another doctor within the same practice, almost as though you feel disloyal to make a switch. You may be worried that you will be singled out as a 'troublemaker' and end up with inferior treatment. This should not happen, but that does not mean you will not worry about it!

How to get the best from your doctor

We all know that doctors are incredibly busy and under constant pressure. So how can we avoid taking them for granted, but at the same time ensure we are getting the best possible treatment?

- *Play by the rules.* Find out about the opening hours of your particular medical practice and all the other rules it operates. You may be provided with a written policy or you may need to ask for it. Also take the time to look at the notices on the waiting-room wall. For example, it may state that you can only expect to see a doctor on a Saturday in an emergency. Find out what the rules are and do not flout them.
- *Try not to present yourself as a 'special case'.* Of course, your illness is special to you and when you feel rotten you want to feel you deserve special attention. But it is wise to see your situation from the other side – to the receptionist you are just another patient. If you constantly ask for special attention, such as wanting to be seen by a doctor at a moment's notice without an appointment or asking for advice over the telephone during busy times, you will not be popular.
- *Avoid calling out the doctor on a home visit* unless it is absolutely necessary. Many people feel they have a 'right' to call out a doctor – after all, if they are 'on call' then it is a doctor's job to see patients who are ill. But some patients abuse this service and it can be very annoying for a doctor to find that a patient has asked for a home visit when their medical problem could have waited until a routine surgery appointment.

Getting the best out of a consultation

Do you ever feel rushed when you meet your doctor? You forget to tell or ask them something important, or find it difficult to remember what was said? The following advice will help you plan ahead and ensure you get the most out of a consultation:

- If you think it would be helpful, make a checklist of what you want to say so you do not forget any of the key points you want to get across.
- Be prepared to describe each individual symptom, what it feels like, how long you have had it, anything that makes the symptom worse or better (such as moving to a different position, eating certain foods or time of eating).

- Allow the doctor thinking time. Do not feel you have to 'fill' every silence with a comment or question.
- Tell the doctor how you feel. Do not forget to describe your emotions as well as your physical symptoms.
- If you do not understand what has been said to you, do not be afraid to say so. Ask for an explanation to be repeated. You could also ask the doctor to write down key words so you can look at them when you get home and discuss them with your family or find out more. Or ask if it is OK if you make brief notes so you can look at them later.
- You could ask your doctor if you could tape-record consultations to listen to at leisure later on. This is a particularly useful way of getting to grips with complex treatment explanations. Your doctor is not obliged to let you do this but may think it is a good idea.
- You may want to consider taking a friend with you to doctors' appointments. This may be a way of helping you feel supported and also a good idea if you tend to forget to ask key questions. A friend will often remember to ask the questions you forget! But as a matter of courtesy ask in advance if your doctor minds.
- If you feel unhappy with the way consultations are going, try to talk about it with your doctor. Remember they may not realize you are unhappy if you do not say so. It is hard to express dissatisfaction, but give the doctor the chance to put things right before you take matters further. Be straightforward. Try saying, 'I find it difficult to say this, but I feel we are not getting on. I don't feel understood/I don't feel what I am saying is understood . . .' Start with how you feel and avoid making accusations.
- Try asking your doctor how he or she is! Being courteous and friendly is not just good manners, it will help put your relationship with your doctor on a sound basis.

What to ask your doctor about medication you are prescribed

If you are prescribed medication, do not forget to ask if there are any side-effects. If side-effects are likely, try to find out how long these could last, how severe they could be, and what you can do about them. You will probably want to ask if the medication you have to take is likely to cure your problem or whether it is designed to treat only the symptoms. Either way, you will probably want to know how long it will take for the medication to be effective. Additionally, you may want to know if there is an optimum time to take the medicine – morning or evening, before, with or after meals – and if it is likely to interfere with any other medicines you are already taking. Do not assume your doctor will remember or look up to see what other medication you are taking. It is always best to remind him or her and ask if it is safe to take new medications prescribed with existing ones. Above all, you will want to find out what the medication is likely to do for you – and if it is really necessary.

How to change your doctor

If you simply do not get on with your doctor, or find he or she is unsympathetic towards you, you may feel your only option is to change to a different doctor. But how do you go about it?

- In the UK, in theory, you can change your doctor without giving a reason although you will almost certainly be asked why you no longer wish to be registered with your present doctor. If you are registered within a group practice, do not forget that you are not obliged to see the same doctor every time. There is no need to think that 'your' doctor will feel you are being disloyal. The practice is likely to have many hundreds, even thousands, of patients and the doctors are far too busy to keep tabs on which doctor each of their patients ends up seeing. It is unlikely anyone will notice if you ask for one particular doctor in preference over another.
- If you want to switch to a different practice, you will need to live within its catchment area. Friends, neighbours or members of a local support group who live close to you may be able to recommend a particular doctor to you.
- Find your medical card (if you cannot find it, then the practice you wish to register with will apply for a duplicate on your behalf) and call in to register. Alternatively you could apply by letter.
- You may be refused on the grounds that the practice is already 'full' or that you do not live in the catchment area. Ask if there is an appeals process.

How to get a second opinion

In the UK, under the Patient's Charter, you do have the right to a second opinion – but only if your doctor agrees it is necessary. You do not have an automatic right to a second opinion and you cannot insist on seeing a particular doctor. If you think you have a good reason for wanting a second opinion and you think this has been unreasonably refused you will be able to take your complaint further. Until April 2002, contact your local Community Health Council (England and Wales). After that date, new Patient Advocacy and Liaison Services should be in place. Also try the Patients Association, a national organization which lobbies for patients' interests (see Resources).

What to do if you have a complaint about your doctor

If you are unhappy with your doctor, for example you think you are receiving poor treatment, then you are entitled to make a complaint. The first step is to talk to your doctor to give him or her at least the chance to put things right. If you are still not happy, then you may wish to consider making a formal complaint. In the UK, ask the receptionist for a copy of the practice's formal complaints procedure which will tell you the steps involved. If they cannot provide you with a step-by-step guide, approach your local health authority and ask them how you should go about it. Complaints relating to the attitude or behaviour of a doctor should be made to the General Medical Council (see Resources).

If you have a complaint about treatment you have received in an NHS hospital, you need to complain directly to the person involved in the first instance, and if you are not happy you can then contact the complaints manager at the NHS trust or health authority concerned. Your local Community Health Council can provide you with a copy of the complaints procedure you should follow.

When making a complaint, be prepared to state:

- the date or dates on which the incident happened;
- the place and time of the incident;
- your hospital number (if you have one);
- the name of the person involved;
- what actually happened;
- what action you think should be taken.

It is best to make a complaint straight away, but in any case you must make a complaint within six months of the incident (or six months after you realize you have something to complain about as long as this is no more than one year after the incident).

14
Managing Work

If you are working for an employer when illness strikes then you may worry about what your rights are. Could you be sacked even though you have a doctor's certificate? Much depends on what kind of employer you have. In general, large employers have guidelines laid down and procedures they follow if employees become chronically ill or sick on a long-term basis. Small employers (with 20 or fewer employees) are likely to be badly hit financially if one member of staff becomes ill and needs frequent absences from work, and so they may be less willing to keep your job open indefinitely.

You may well have rights under legislation so do check. In the UK, the Disability Discrimination Act (DDA) 1995 defines disablement as 'a physical or mental impairment which has a substantial and long term adverse effect on your ability to carry out normal day-to-day activities'. This includes sensory impairments such as loss of vision, but also progressive conditions and those which are characterized by a number of cumulative effects such as pain or fatigue. You do not have to register as a disabled person to have rights under the Act and the Disability Rights Commission has been set up by the government to ensure the Act is enforced and provide all the information you need (see Resources).

So what is likely to happen at work if you become ill? Before deciding whether to dismiss or retire you on the grounds of ill health, a responsible employer should:

- Consider if a different type of work might suit you better.
- Consult you about your illness and discuss with you how this affects the company.
- Consider asking you to see a company doctor or independent medical adviser so a medical report can be prepared and your condition and prospects assessed and then give you the chance to comment on the report.
- Make a decision as to whether or not your attendance record is likely to improve and decide if it is reasonable to dismiss you in the circumstances.

You should not be sacked without any warning or caution – responsible employers should talk to you about their concerns and give you the chance to respond. They are likely to take into account factors such as the type of illness you have and the likelihood of it recurring or other illnesses arising as a result; the number and length of absences; how important the work is perceived to be; the impact of your absences on other workers and the impact of your absences on the company. Large companies almost certainly have a policy they are required to follow. Contact the Human Resources department and ask if you can have a copy. If you are sacked on the grounds of ill health, you should be entitled to the statutory notice period at full pay and any holiday pay you are entitled to.

Telling people at work

One of your biggest concerns may be telling friends and colleagues what is happening to you, especially if you have only recently become ill. You may wonder if it is better not to tell everyone the details in case they treat you differently – perhaps the thought of people making allowances for you or constantly asking how you are and so on fills you with horror.

On the other hand, if your illness does necessitate regular days off because you are unwell or have hospital appointments to keep, then it may be wise to tell your immediate colleagues so they know why you are absent. It might be better for them to know the truth rather than run the risk of inaccurate speculation or gossip.

Talk to your manager, if you have one, about your fears and worries and see if there is any way your work can be covered in your absence so the company does not suffer too badly. If you take a responsible and sympathetic attitude towards the impact of your sickness absences on the company, then perhaps your company will take a responsible and sympathetic attitude towards your illness – although of course they may not.

If you are away for a long period of time but hope to return to work either to the same company or to a similar job in a different company, it would be worthwhile keeping up contacts as much as possible while you are away. Keep abreast of what is going on – read professional journals if appropriate and, if you are up to it, keep in contact with colleagues by phone so it will be a little easier to make a smooth transition back to the workplace.

George, 47, a contract manager from Oxfordshire, was devastated when he discovered that he had kidney disease ten years ago: 'When I was told that I would need regular dialysis and would have to go on the kidney transplant waiting list so many fears went through my mind. As well as worrying about the effect it would have on my family I was concerned that it might mean the end of my career. In fact my employers have been fantastic. I was lucky enough to need only two five-hour sessions of dialysis a week and I opted for evening appointments so it didn't interfere too much with my job. You get to know the hospital staff so well they become almost like a second family! But it did mean I could no longer travel abroad and that was hard to come to terms with as it was a part of my job I enjoyed. I waited four years for a transplant – I knew the call could come at any time and in the end it came late one evening after my wife and I had just come back from an evening out. The phone rang at 11.30 p.m., I was in hospital by 1 a.m. and having the operation the next morning at 8.30. My employers were great because they knew a transplant would mean I would be out of action for about three months, literally without any warning. When the call comes, you can't think about it, you just have to jump at the opportunity. Fortunately, both my family and my employers have been completely supportive which has helped me get through it. I think it helps if you keep them informed at every stage so they understand what you're going through.'

Returning to work

If you are, or have been, ill and you are looking for a new job then find out who is the best person to give you accurate information about how to go about it. In the UK, check out your nearest Disability Employment Adviser (DEA) who is based at your local Job Centre. Your DEA will also be able to advise you about current schemes and will have a knowledge of disability issues in relation to education and training opportunities. Or contact your local Employment Service, part of the government Department for Education and Employment (DfEE) and responsible for running Job Centres. If you are out of work or have been made redundant, you could telephone Employment Service Direct (see Resources).

How honest should you be?

Should you tell a prospective employer that you have a disability or chronic illness? This is a difficult one, especially if you have an illness that is not 'visible' and you feel it does not affect your ability to do the job. There is no right or wrong answer. Many people hide their illnesses from their employers because they are afraid that if they do not, they would lose their job even though their illness does not affect their performance. It is certainly true that some employers are more likely to discriminate against you if they know you have an illness. Even if you explain that it will not affect the way you do your job, their perception may be that you are a potential liability and, given the choice, they would rather employ someone who has no health problems.

In the UK, one good reason for telling an employer the truth at the outset is that your employment might then be covered by the Disability Discrimination Act 1995. If you declare your disability and feel you have been treated unfairly in the application process you could make a complaint to an employment tribunal. It means an employer cannot lawfully refuse to employ you because of your disability without good reason. If you do not disclose your disability and then an employer feels you are unable to do the work, they may have grounds to sack you. Another obvious reason to declare your health problems from the outset is that it might help explain any long gaps in your CV.

It is also worth bearing in mind that not all employers will see every type of disability as a disadvantage. It is up to you to think laterally about what your illness or disability has taught you and the skills you have acquired directly as a result that could be useful in a workplace setting. For example if you have restricted mobility it may have given you the chance to develop an interest in information technology. Years of trying to find out about a rare disorder may have helped you develop excellent research skills using the Internet. By emphasizing skills you have acquired as you have tried to overcome your illness or disability will help you present yourself as determined and an asset rather than a liability, although in practice you may still come up against unhelpful attitudes and discrimination.

When you start a new job

If you have decided to tell people about your illness from the outset, then it makes sense to educate them as to what your illness means to you and the impact it is likely to have on your work. Do not assume people will know how it affects you. Remember that many people will feel awkward and may pretend to understand when in reality they are confused and embarrassed. Take the initiative and explain if you have particular requirements or needs – most people will be only too happy to help if they fully understand the situation. And do not forget that good humour goes a long way – it will help break down barriers, especially if people feel awkward.

Don't forget that you may be entitled to sick pay, subject to the length of your employment and National Insurance contributions. Check with your employer.

15

Making the Most of Services Available

You may find there are a variety of care services you could take advantage of. In the UK, these may be offered by private or voluntary organizations, your local authority or the National Health Service. What is available is largely a matter of luck. Some areas have lots of services and things going on. In other areas the provision is patchy. The first port of call should be your area social services department (or social work department in Scotland) who should be able to tell you what is available. Your local Citizens' Advice Bureau will also be a mine of information.

What is available in your area?

Examples of services that might be available include:

- *District nurses* provide some nursing care at home. They can also arrange delivery of special equipment such as incontinence aids.
- *Health visitors* provide information and advice on services available in your area and other practical advice.
- *Hospital after-care schemes* provide short-term help to assist you when you first leave hospital.
- *Physiotherapists* help with mobility problems and provide treatment and advice on pain relief as well as advice about special equipment that might help you.
- *Sleeping-in service* allows a carer a night off.
- *Care attendant schemes* are mainly aimed at the disabled and elderly to enable you to stay in your own home.
- *Home helps* assist with domestic tasks including shopping or some personal care.
- *Good neighbour schemes* are usually set up on a local, informal basis. Volunteers might be able to do odd jobs, help with gardening or read to you.
- *Meals on wheels* ensure you receive a hot meal on some days.
- *Hospital car service or medical escort service* help if you are unable to get to hospital appointments on your own.

The best advice is to find out what is available in your area, and then do consider taking advantage of the services that you feel would most benefit *you*.

Advocate schemes

You may find that there is a citizen advocacy scheme running in your area. These schemes started in the United States and are becoming popular in the UK too. The idea is to help people who are disabled or disadvantaged in some way to get their voice heard. If you feel that you need someone to speak up for you at a hospital appointment or during a complaints procedure you could ask to be assigned an advocate – basically a volunteer who will represent your interests. You can find out more about advocate schemes at your local Citizens' Advice Bureau.

Could a self-help group help you?

Some people find the idea of joining a self-help group less than appealing. From the outside, it might seem that it is just an excuse for people to get together and have a good moan about their lot. It is true that not everyone feels at home in a self-help group. But on the other hand many people who thought they would never fit in, or that it would not have anything to offer, go on to find that it becomes a lifeline.

What is a self-help group? There is no single definition and no two groups are the same. Some are small and reliant on a handful of members to disseminate basic information. Others are large, well-organized and well-financed groups with hundreds of volunteers and beautifully produced advice leaflets and newsletters. Some are very locally based, others are national organizations, usually charities, with local groups all over the country. Some operate simply, just talking to people over the phone, while others arrange regular meetings, days out or even holiday get-togethers for members.

Usually you will find that you can join either for free or for a very modest fee and then decide for yourself how much you want to be involved. You might prefer to make contact only when you have a specific question or worry, or you might end up taking on a role you never thought you would enjoy, such as talking to others about your experiences. The important thing to remember is that the choice is yours – no one is going to force you to rattle a collecting tin or speak in a group if you do not want to. So it makes sense to at least see what is on offer before you rule it out completely.

Many people find that meeting other people who know what they are going through is a tremendous help. That does not mean you have to spend all your time moaning or being sympathetic! But knowing there are other people who really understand the problems you are facing and the particular emotions you are going through can give you an enormous boost, especially if you are going through a bad patch. Just knowing that you can phone someone who will not think you are being a nuisance and is genuinely sympathetic, in the way only someone who has been through the same ordeal as you, can really help.

To find out if there is a self-help group in your area, contact the national charity concerned with your particular health problem (if there is one), look at local notice-boards, ask your local doctor, health visitor or district nurse or at your nearest library, or get hold of a copy of the *Voluntary Agencies Directory* which is published annually by the National Council for Voluntary Organizations (see Resources).

A world of possibilities on the Internet

Another idea if you have a computer and you are wired up to the Internet is to see if there are any news or discussion groups specifically designed for your health problem. Even if you suffer from something quite rare you could find there is a group already in existence with participants from all over the world. It will cost you nothing over and above what you pay already to surf the net.

In the UK, if you do not already have a computer and like the sound of this, you could try it out for a modest fee at one of the many Internet cafes around the country, or find out at your local library if they have any Internet facilities available to the public.

How to locate a suitable news or discussion group

Choose a search engine (such as www.yahoo.com); then simply type in the name of the illness you are suffering from followed by the word 'newsgroups', for example 'multiple sclerosis newsgroups'. It may take a few minutes to sift through all the entries to find a newsgroup as there will be all sorts of webpages on offer, including charities and products relating to the topic you wish to discuss as well as websites set up by individuals who have something to say on the subject. But there should be at least one newsgroup as well as other sites you like the sound of. When you locate a newsgroup, you will be able to see all the contributions posted on the group over the past few days or weeks. In popular groups, you may find that every day there are literally hundreds of messages available to read.

You can simply read what other people have written – usually someone will post either a question or an observation and then other people post their replies or their observations. So any one question may generate dozens or hundreds of answers. There will be instructions to follow if you want to post your own question or respond to a message or question posted by someone else. You may find that quite a lot of what is posted is not relevant to you, but makes interesting reading anyway. Or some may be a bit tedious!

The good thing about discussion groups is that they are constantly changing and constantly updated, so you do not have time to get bored. And you can often read all the messages posted by one person so you can get a feel of whether they are an active member of the group and the kinds of advice or comments they usually contribute. Often people write up with ideas on which treatments have and have not worked for them or how they have dealt with side-effects. It is a great way of asking others for advice or getting reassurance without having to leave your own home.

A warning

The disadvantage of a news or discussion group is, of course, that you have no idea at all who posted the messages and therefore no idea if the information or advice contained in it is accurate. There have been reports in the press that some people pretend to have illnesses or even feign medical qualifications so it is best to be very cautious. See any information you find in a discussion group as a starting point only and do not act on it unless you have discussed it with a doctor you trust first. Be wary and never disclose personal details such as your telephone number, home or e-mail address in a message.

On a more optimistic note, it can be a tremendous boost if you post a message to a discussion group and find, when you next log in, that you have 20 or 30 sympathetic replies waiting for you.

16

Looking After Yourself

When illness strikes, you may begin to think about your health in a way you never have before. You might become 'tuned in' to parts of your body you were barely aware of, and for the first time in your life you may be rethinking what you eat, how much you exercise, how stressed you are, the medications you take, and so on. One positive side of illness is that it may act as a 'wake up' call to help you look after your health in a more positive and pro-active way.

One problem is that if you feel unwell, you may have less energy than usual to devote to looking after yourself. But take a look at the following list of ideas and see if there is anything you might be able to do that could help.

Look good, feel good

It may seem trite but there is more than a grain of truth in the saying, 'Look good, feel good'. If you look your best, then somehow you feel better inside. The smallest things can help give you a boost, like trawling through your wardrobe and ferreting out something you have not worn for a while, treating yourself to something new or having your hair done. Try treating yourself to a massage or pampering yourself with a luxurious bubble bath at home or curling up with a favourite book or video – whatever makes you feel good. Even if you are housebound and rarely have visitors, you will find that making an extra effort every day to look your best is an important morale-booster, however silly it may seem. No one is suggesting you wear the family jewels or don a sequinned dinner jacket, but taking the trouble to look as good as you can will really help make you feel better.

Listen to your body

One of the best ways you can start caring for yourself is to start listening to your body. We have all heard stories of men and women who ignored the warning signs and carried on in stressful jobs, working late, rushing around and not eating properly only to be struck down with a heart attack. For some people, becoming ill is a chance to reassess their lives and rethink priorities.

One thing you can do right now is to start to listen to your body. What is it telling you? Should you slow down or do a bit more? Should you relax and learn to say no more often, or is it time to take on a bit more responsibility? Do you need to eat less fatty food and more fruit and vegetables? Do you need to cut down on alcohol or rethink the painkillers you take? Are you doing anything that is making you feel worse instead of better? Once you start to listen to what your body is trying to tell you, then you will become more in tune with your body and you will intuitively know what is best for you.

Eat as well as you can

Eating a good diet is vital at any time, but especially when you are ill. There has been a lot of controversy about organic food and whether or not it is better for you. It stands to reason that food produced with fewer chemicals and pesticides is liable to be better for you than conventionally produced food. Unfortunately organic food is more expensive, not least because production costs are higher. But at the very least, you should aim to eat at least five portions of fruit and vegetables a day whether organic or conventionally produced.

Listen to what your body wants to eat. We tend to get out of the habit of eating when we are hungry and so have lost touch with our instincts about what we should and should not eat. If you instinctively feel you are eating too much fatty food or not eating enough fruit and vegetables, then adjust your diet. Clues that your diet needs adjusting include excessive wind, feelings of bloatedness or food cravings.

If you have a poor appetite or eating problems because of your illness, then do the best you can. Eat small, appetizing, regular meals and make them as attractive and nutritious as you can to gain the most benefit. This is very hard, especially if you do not feel like eating, but try to keep your strength up as much as you can during these difficult days. If you have family or friends who like to cook, ask if someone else will cook you something from time to time. It is sometimes easier to eat what someone else has cooked.

In a nutshell, you should aim to cut down on saturated fats (mainly found in meat and dairy products), eat more complex carbohydrates (brown rice, wholewheat pasta, wholewheat bread, beans and pulses), eat fewer sugary foods, eat more fresh fruit and vegetables, eat fewer convenience foods (which are often higher in fat and contain less-desirable ingredients such as hydrogenated vegetable oil or monosodium glutamate), and more oily fish such as mackerel, herrings and sardines which are rich in omega-3 essential fatty acids and are known to help prevent heart disease.

Ask your doctor about exercise

Exercise is a great stress-reliever as well as having a number of other health benefits. It helps lower blood pressure, keep your heart and other muscles healthy, lifts your mood and makes you feel generally good about yourself. Obviously your ability to exercise will depend on the kind of illness you have and its severity but you may be able to do more than you think. Why not talk to your doctor about what would be safe for you to try? (See p. 53 for some ideas.)

Learn to relax

One way to relax is to find a quiet spot and do a little meditation. Start by noticing how you breathe. Try this exercise:

Lie down and place your hand on your diaphragm – the area just above your navel. Notice what happens when you breathe in and out. If your abdomen expands and your hand rises as you breathe in, you are breathing in the best possible way. When we are stressed we tend to breathe 'through' the chest, in rapid, shallow breaths which only partly fill the lungs with air. Do not try to force your breathing. After all, breathing is the most natural thing in the world and it happens whether we like it or not! Just be aware of your breath. It might help if, as your tummy rises and falls, you close your eyes and think of the sea washing in to the shore over the shingle, and then out again, in a continuous, rhythmic movement. You should find this exercise very relaxing. Even at odd moments during the day, you can draw your attention back to your breathing.

A purpose in life

Psychologists have concluded that when we feel connected to something, we feel more of a purpose in our life. Research shows that people who are married experience less ill health than those who are not. But you do not have to be married to feel 'connected'. Research shows that people who have a religious faith enjoy a sense of belonging and may experience better health. Having friends is important too. It is difficult if you feel unwell and have little energy – but it is worth the effort. Do not allow your illness to dominate your life to the extent you are alone, all the time. And if all else fails, do consider getting a pet. Knowing that, however ill you are, another creature is relying on you for care and food can give you a reason to get up in the morning. No one is suggesting you opt for a high-maintenance animal. If you are frail or unable to move about, forget giving a home to a collie dog, however appealing! A cat is ideal as they are quite independent, but can be very loving when it suits them!

I used to be a person who could never understand why anyone liked cats, but after one was foisted on me I soon became smitten and now Lottie is the love of my life (after my husband, of course!). But even a humble goldfish can be fun and rewarding to look after. You can become surprisingly fond of a goldfish!

Time to learn

Even if you feel too unwell to work, this may be an opportunity for you to consider learning something new. There are many open or distance-learning options – studying at home at your own pace. You could choose a topic you would like to study for pleasure or with a view to acquiring a qualification that might help you gain employment at some point in the future. These days many colleges offer open and distance-learning courses – the college nearest to you may offer a range of options. In the UK you could contact the National Extension College, the Open College of the Arts or the Open University (see Resources for addresses). It is worth noting that it is really worth trying to find a new interest that totally absorbs you. One psychologist (Csikszentmihalyi 1992) claimed that if you can become absorbed in something in such a way that it takes all your concentration and you almost 'lose yourself' in what you are doing (he called it 'flow' experience), then it can enhance your feeling of well-being.

17

A Chapter for Carers

In the UK, one in four adults is a carer and almost everyone agrees it is one of the most difficult jobs in the world. A survey in the year 2000 by the St John's Ambulance, a UK-based charity, has found that levels of stress, depression and illness in carers are rising. Nearly a third of carers say they are suffering from stress or depression or both and nearly a half say they suffer from chronic fatigue.

What is it about being a carer that is so hard? First there is the physical strain. If you are a wife and a mother, or a husband and a father, and perhaps running a home as well, then caring for someone who is ill can be exhausting. On top of the everyday or mundane tasks that need to be done such as shopping and cooking, you may have to lift the person you are caring for – in and out of bed or on to a chair with all the bending, reaching and stretching it involves.

But it is often the *emotional* exhaustion that goes unnoticed. It is hard to explain to someone who has not been a carer why the job takes its toll. It is partly the weight of sheer responsibility, the relentlessness of the job, having to worry day in, day out about someone, wanting to do your best and perhaps feeling it is never quite good enough. Above all, you wish you could wave a magic wand and make it all better, not for yourself, but for the person who is sick. And there are so many mixed feelings to make sense of. One minute you can feel incredible sympathy for their plight but the next feel irritated because they are walking so slowly or do not seem to be grateful for what you do.

You know they are not 'putting it on' or exaggerating their symptoms or doing it just to annoy you, yet sometimes you feel annoyed despite yourself. There are times you probably feel like crying, 'What about *me*?' It can also be depressing to be in an atmosphere where illness is ever-present. You may get tired of hearing about the person's symptoms and long to have a conversation about something ordinary or interesting for a change. Yet all the time you know that, to the person who is ill, you are a lifeline. You might be the only person in their life who truly cares or understands and that can be a burden in itself because it makes it harder to walk away or take time out.

Sometimes it is difficult because the person you are caring for is not all sweetness and light! Just because you are a great carer does not mean the person you care for will always be grateful. Moreover, the fact you are trying to help someone does not necessarily mean they want your help or agree you are helping in the right way.

In some ways, carers suffer almost as much as the person who is ill. Watching someone suffer and being unable to help them or relieve their pain is a frightening, horribly distressing experience. You may feel unsettled by the way your attitudes have changed. Some find that where they had a strong religious faith before, now they are asking more questions. Others find it is only their faith that is helping them through.

Ron, aged 80, looks after his wife Winifred, 78, who has Alzheimer's disease. For Ron, one of the hardest things to cope with is knowing that Winifred will never get better: 'With Alzheimer's there is no light at the end of the tunnel – it's difficult to accept that no matter how well she is cared for, she will only get worse. I can't bear the thought that I might become ill and be unable to look after her. But we are very lucky in many ways. Winifred's main problem at the moment is that she is forgetful which means I always have to be very concerned about safety – making sure she has not left the gas on, for example – but she is still physically fit and we can talk about her illness. But I am realistic enough to know that one day she may deteriorate to the point where she doesn't even realize she is ill. I cope by taking one day at a time. I think it is very important for carers to look after themselves, to maintain some independence and stay in touch with what is going on in the world, so I make a point of reading a newspaper from cover to cover every day, plus I have joined a bridge club to make sure that at least one day a week I get out and meet people and follow an interest of my own. I also think that meeting other carers can be a tremendous help – but it is frustrating when it is assumed that all carers are a homogenous bunch of people. We're all different! It may take time to find other like-minded carers who have similar interests or a similar outlook – but it's worth persevering in order to feel you have found someone who knows what you are going through.'

To be a carer or not to be a carer?

What if you have just been told that someone you love is seriously ill? You may be in the process of trying to decide if you should help care for that person. The enormity of this decision cannot be underestimated and it is bound to be a very stressful time for you. There are likely to be many practical issues to be thought through. For example, will it mean having someone to live with you full-time or going to live with them? Will it mean you have to consider giving up your job? Will you have to change your current routine or reorganize current responsibilities in order to take on board this new commitment?

And there are far-reaching emotional issues too. You may wonder if you can cope with the stress. Perhaps you feel you ought to take on the responsibility, but in your heart of hearts wish you could refuse. And you may feel resentful or angry that it is you who seems to have to shoulder the burden while others in the family do not seem to be doing their bit.

Finding a way through this emotional maelstrom will inevitably be hard. However responsible or sorry or upset you feel for someone, you cannot ignore your own feelings. You have a right to a life too, and you cannot sacrifice yours entirely to help someone else if, in the long run, it is going to make you ill or be impossible for you to cope.

Ultimately, you can only do what you can do. You can do your best – and that is all. If you know deep down that you are going to find it too difficult to cope, then it is better to find a way to say so from the outset. Do not wait for others to offer to take on some responsibility. Tell them what you are prepared to do and what you are not prepared to do and ask for help to 'plug the gaps'. No one should think badly of you for being honest about what you can offer and what you cannot. And if they do think badly of you, then it is their problem, not yours. All you can do is your best – no less and no more.

If others are not pulling their weight

A common problem that can arise in families is that one person feels they are shouldering too much of the responsibility of caring while others are shirking their duty. It can be annoying if you feel you are putting yourself out to care for a family member while a sibling or someone else in the family does not seem to be doing their 'fair share'. But this can be an unhelpful way to look at the situation. Being a carer is such a personal decision that it is not helpful to think in terms of what is fair and what is not. It is best to concentrate only on what you can do and do what feels comfortable for you. Refuse to allow yourself to be drawn into judging someone else's contribution and you will save yourself a lot of heartache.

Yes, it is hard, and there will be times when you are tired and fed up, when you feel annoyed that someone else in the family seems content to do the bare minimum or uses the lamest excuse not to do the smallest good deed. But getting upset or having an argument about it probably will not change a thing, and will just add to the stress you are under. Their motives for not helping may be that they just cannot cope emotionally. Or it may be that they are lazy or uncaring. They may be good at simply saying no, whereas you always end up saying 'yes' even though you would rather refuse! Or they may use the excuse of being too busy, living too far away, having too many other commitments, and so on. Ultimately, analysing and fretting about their reasons will not make you feel any better. The best plan is to decide that you will do what you feel able to do, no more and no less. Others will have to make – and live with – their own decision.

Terminal illness

What if the person who needs care is terminally ill? Outsiders may imagine that if you are being asked to care for someone for a finite period of time, then it should be more manageable. But, of course, it is not as simple as that. Discovering someone you love is terminally ill is one of the worst shocks imaginable. My mum was 67 when one day she noticed that her skin had turned a little yellow. She had been feeling fine, other than a slight pain in the tummy, coping with a full-time job and looking forward to a rather late retirement. A routine visit to the hospital was arranged to investigate what the problem might be and then, suddenly, she was taken into hospital for an 'exploratory' operation. Both my mum and I were both convinced she must have a gall-bladder problem as she still felt, and looked, well.

While Mum waited for the operation I started to read my medical books to see if I could fathom out what was wrong with her. When I saw the words 'cancer of the pancreas', I realized with horror that this might be what was wrong with my mum. I read that there were few warning signs and by the time the disease struck it was generally too late for anything other than palliative care – and the prognosis was very poor.

I was distraught. I sat outside the operating theatre, watched the orderlies wheel my mum in for her operation and waited for what seemed like hours for news. Then the surgeon emerged and sat beside me on the cold bench in the long hospital corridor. My worst fears were confirmed and he added there was absolutely nothing that could be done. When I asked how long my mother would live, he replied possibly six months, but more likely three. The shock was almost unbearable.

It would be a few hours before my mum would recover from the anaesthetic, so I drove home in a daze and I put very loud music on the stereo to drown out the sound of my weeping. I cried my heart out, wailing long, loud wails, frightening noises I had never heard before emanating from somewhere deep in the pit of my stomach. And then I had to dry my eyes, wash my face and wonder how on earth I could face my dear mum, knowing that she was dying.

At first I did not want her to be told the truth – I know now that this is a common reaction in this situation – because I could not bear the truth myself. The surgeon said they would tell her 'if she asked the right questions', but she never did, convinced she had a mere problem with her gall-bladder. After all, apart from the trauma of the anaesthetic and operation, she felt fine.

But when she was discharged from hospital it quickly became apparent that I should have allowed the surgeon to tell her. Suddenly she was talking about the future, about going back to work and what she would do when she retired and it seemed wrong and unfair for her to go on without knowing the truth. I also knew that it would be difficult to keep up the pretence. Supposing when she did finally realize, she wanted to know why no one had told her?

In the end, I told her myself that she had cancer, convincing myself that perhaps she had already guessed. But she was totally stunned, especially as it dawned that she was being denied any kind of treatment and she must have been sent home to die. Even when she asked me the question I dreaded, yet was so unprepared to answer, she had hope in her eyes. When she asked me how long she would live, in retrospect I think she still thought it would be years. But somehow I found myself telling her the truth, bluntly, cruelly.

I don't know why I didn't break it gently or offer some hope that maybe she could fight the cancer. Instead I must have seemed uncaring, hiding behind a business-like mask when inside I was already mourning and crying like a baby. If only we could have cried together but I was too afraid, totally overwhelmed by the horror of it all, and gripped by my own inadequacy and helplessness, so I didn't reach out to her when she needed me most.

She cried briefly and I will always regret that I didn't rush to her side and give her a huge cuddle. Somehow I was rooted to the spot, terrified of breaking down and not being able to stop crying yet longing to sweep her up in my arms and hold her. I still wonder if I did the right thing to tell her. It wasn't as if she wanted to take a world cruise or anything like that. I sometimes think she gave up there and then. I had offered her no hope because I felt at that time there was none. If I had known then what I know now, I would have done things so differently. We could have gone to the Bristol Cancer Help Centre for the marvellous support they offer. We could have got some comfort from alternative therapies, been open to new ideas or found people who had the same disease but defied the statistics. We could have tried to fight the disease together instead of just giving up at the first hurdle. The statistics were stark enough – and almost three months to the day of being diagnosed, she died.

The last few weeks were harrowing. We were trying to look forward to Christmas the best we could and Mum was looking forward to a special dance on Christmas Eve – she had always loved ballroom dancing. I remember going shopping with her and seeing her trying on a new dress and despairing at how it didn't fit her. She had always prided herself on her smart appearance but now the reality was beginning to sink in and we were both suddenly aware of how much weight she had lost and how skeletal she looked as the dress hung awkwardly and horribly on her bony shoulders. When she went back into the fitting room to get changed, I ran out of the shop, unable to control the tears but afraid to show her my distress in case it distressed her.

On Christmas Eve we had a wonderful evening together, then she felt tired and went to bed. Within hours she deteriorated and became bed-bound, needing all care. It was clear that she had only a few days to live. Yet though I was her only daughter and loved her very much, I found that I could not face being with her at the end. I desperately wanted to hold her hand, wash her, do everything for her and be with her when she died. But I just could not do it. It wasn't that I found it distasteful, but I was in such emotional turmoil that I found it unbearable. I remember feeling so upset when I bought her a beaker to drink her tea from. It had seemed like a good idea because she was so frail she could not manage a cup. But she raged against using the plastic beaker, angry that anyone should imagine that she would need to resort to a beaker and determined to drink from a cup even though she spilt her tea down her nightie again and again. She cried in her frustration, angry that her life had come to this, and to see her distress was so very heartbreaking.

When her doctor asked if I would like her to go into a hospice, I struggled with my conscience and eventually said 'yes'. In the event, my mum died the night before she was due to be admitted. Her sister had moved in with her by now and for that I was grateful but even so it turned out that no one was with her when she died. For my part, I found it too hard to be there for her, frozen with selfish fear and grief, longing to be there at the end to hold her hand and be with her when she died, but terrified. So in the end she died alone.

Yet, at the time, I know I did my best. I wasn't capable of doing more because I found it too horrific, too emotionally upsetting. Yes, it seems selfish and pathetic – not least because, after all, it was my mum who was dying, it was my mum who was suffering and my mum who was alone while I was hiding away feeling sorry for myself. And, believe me, if I could turn back the clock I would do so.

A few years later, my mum's sister became terminally ill with lung cancer and I was able to care for her at the end. She did go into a hospice, but I visited every day and I was with her when she died. It was the most incredible experience. Above all, I was so pleased for my aunt that she was not alone and that I could hold her hand and stroke her forehead and whisper that I loved her at the moment of death. All the things I would love to have done for my mum if I had only had the courage.

Perhaps I could do it for my aunt because although we were very close, it wasn't the same as having to do it for my mum. It was very hard and upsetting, but it was bearable. Above all, I was so glad I was able to be there for *her*.

Although I regret not being there for my mum, I cannot hate myself for it because, ultimately, I know I did the absolute best I could *at the time* in the worst of circumstances. And it taught me two important lessons. First, that it is very easy to criticize the actions or non-actions of others, but until you have walked in their shoes, it is wrong to judge. Second, do not spend your life feeling guilty. Just do the best you can and if sometimes you cannot do what you expect of yourself or what others expect of you, then forgive yourself.

And if you are looking after someone who is terminally ill, my heart goes out to you. Make sure you get the help and support you need. Talk to someone about how you feel. Be gentle on yourself, especially if you are finding it hard.

A 'good' death

What makes a 'good' death? For many it means not being in pain, and being involved in making decisions about their treatment – even declining treatment if preferred. It means having the chance to put their affairs in order; and knowing what to expect when death seems imminent. Will family and friends be allowed to be present? For many people it is very important to have the chance to say a proper goodbye. And for some it is important to know that others appreciate what they have done in their life, and know they will be remembered in a proper and appropriate way. It may seem macabre, but it is very important for some people to be involved in planning their own funeral.

If you are able to help allay fears and provide the help a dying person needs to fulfil all of these, it is something you will always be glad you did. It takes courage, and you may not be able to do it, but if you can, you will look back and know you did your very best and helped make someone's last few days or weeks as good as they could be.

Getting a break from caring

If you are a carer, finding time for yourself is a big issue. In addition to your role as a carer, you are probably juggling many aspects of your own life, with a family and home of your own to care for as well. It is vital to find time for yourself occasionally, to recharge your batteries and keep stress levels at bay.

You can tell if it is time for a break from caring if you dread seeing the person, you feel resentful, anxious or angry about what you have to do, you feel tired all the time, or have no time to yourself, you know you are neglecting your own health, or others constantly tell you that you are doing too much – or you feel depressed.

So do make the effort to find out about opportunities for care in your area so that you can have regular breaks. In the UK, for example, you may find:

- Day centres may be run by your local authority or by voluntary organizations in your area.
- Lunch clubs are run mainly for older people or ethnic groups and may provide activities as well as a meal. Contact Age Concern to see if there is one in your area.
- Day hospitals may be available in some areas and are run by the NHS to provide rehabilitation services.

- Overnight or respite care may be available for a few days in a residential home, hospital, nursing home or hospice. Your local authority social services department (at your county council, unitary council or London borough) will be able to advise. In Northern Ireland, contact your local Health and Social Services Board or in Scotland your nearest Social Work Department for advice.
- Sitting services are provided in some areas to provide care attendants to take over care for a few hours so you can have a break. Contact Crossroads – Caring for Carers or ask at your local authority social services department.

In certain circumstances you may be entitled to some of the following:

- District nursing help with tasks such as changing dressings or giving injections;
- help with laundry;
- extra equipment in the home;
- chiropody, physiotherapy, occupational therapy or speech therapy services (some may be available in the home if it is impossible for the person you care for to get out);
- home visits for dental care;
- specialist nursing support from Community Mental Health Nurses or Community Learning Disability Nurses;
- extra nursing help and equipment if the person you care for is terminally ill;
- meals on wheels.

For more information contact the Carers National Association (see Resources). To find out more about what local voluntary organizations offer in your area, contact your local Council for Voluntary Service (look in your local phone directory or ask at the Citizens' Advice Bureau). The Health Information Service (see Resources) can also give information about many aspects of health, services and voluntary organizations in your area.

Carers' assessment

In the UK, the Carers (Recognition and Services) Act 1995 gives carers various rights and entitlements and requires local authorities to assess individual carers' needs. This involves a meeting between you and a care manager or social worker so you have the chance to say what you want about your situation and the person you care for. If the new Carers and Disabled Children's Bill becomes law, your needs as a carer will be taken into account and you will be entitled in some situations to buy in help in order to have a break. At the moment, however, and in practice, carers find it very difficult to get any help at all in some areas.

Part 5
Resources

While this section aims to be as helpful as possible, there is not sufficient space to include every charity or every type of illness. I apologize if the charity you are trying to locate is not mentioned. Some helplines are free, some are available at local call rate and some at a premium rate. Not all helplines are available on a 24-hour basis. For more information contact the individual charity concerned.

Benefits

Look in your phone book under 'Benefits Agency' for your nearest social security office.

There is a special enquiry line for those with disabilities. Call 0800 882200. If you have a textphone, call 0800 243355.

The Northern Ireland Benefit Enquiry Line is on 0800 220674, or if you have a textphone, 0800 243787.

You can find detailed information on financial help for people with illness and disability in *The Disability Rights Handbook* which is published annually by the Disability Alliance, Universal House, 88–94 Wentworth Street, London E1 7SA; tel: 020 7247 8776.

Carers

Carers National Association, Ruth Pitter House, 20–25 Glasshouse Yard, London EC1A 4JT.
Tel: 0207 490 8818
Helpline: 0808 808 7777
www.carersuk.demon.co.uk

Complementary medicine

General

British Complementary Medicine Association, Kensington House, 33 Imperial Square, Cheltenham GL50 1QZ.
Tel: 01242 519911
www.bcma.co.uk

British Holistic Medical Association, 59 Lansdowne Place, Hove, East Sussex BN3 1FL.
Tel: 01273 725951
www.bhma.org
(Runs courses to encourage self-healing, provides self-help tapes and can supply a list of practitioners.)

The Foundation for Integrated Medicine, International House, 59 Compton Road, London N1 2YT.
Tel: 020 7688 1881
www.fimed.org
(Cannot supply list of individual practitioners, but provides details about governing bodies for individual therapies.)

The Institute for Complementary Medicine, PO Box 194, London SE16 7QZ.
Tel: 020 7237 5165
www.icmedicine.co.uk
(Can supply a list of practitioners in your area.)

Acupuncture

British Acupuncture Council, 63 Jeddo Road, London W12 9HQ.
Tel: 020 8735 0400
www.acupuncture.org.uk

The British Medical Acupuncture Society, Unit 12, Marbury House Farm, Higher Whitley, Warrington, Cheshire WA4 4QW.
Tel: 01925 730727
www.medical-acupuncture.co.uk
(Can supply a list of medically qualified doctors with additional acupuncture qualifications.)

Chiropractic

Chiropractic Patients' Association, 8 Centre One, Lysander Way, Old Sarum, Salisbury SP4 6BU.
Tel: 01722 415027

Homeopathy

British Homeopathic Association, 15 Clerkenwell Close, London EC1R 0AA.
Tel: 020 7566 7800
www.trusthomeopathy.org

Education

National Extension College, The Michael Young Centre, Cambridge CB2 2HN.
Tel: 01223 450200
www.nec.ac.uk

Open College of the Arts, Unit 1B, Redbrooke Business Park, Wilthorpe Road, Barnsley S75 1JN.
Tel: 0800 731 2116
www.oca-uk.com

Open University, Walton Hall, Milton Keynes MK7 6AA.
Tel: 01908 653231
www.open.ac.uk

Medical information and complaints

Department of Health, Public Enquiry Office, Richmond House, 79 Whitehall, London SW1A 2NL.
Tel: 020 7210 4850
www.doh.gov.uk

Disability Rights Commission, Freepost,
MID 02164, Stratford upon Avon CV37 9BR.
Helpline: 08457 622633
Minicom: 08457 622644
www.drc-gb.org

General Medical Council (GMC), 178–202 Great Portland Street, London W1W 5JE.
Tel: 020 7580 7642
www.gmc-uk.org

Health Information Service
Freephone: 0800 665544

NHS Direct
Tel: 0845 464748
(24-hour helpline led by nurses who can give advice and health information, but may not be available in every area.)
www.nhsdirect.nhs.uk

The Patients Association, PO Box 935, Harrow, Middlesex HA1 3YJ.
Tel: 020 8423 9111
www.patients-association.com

Women's Health, 52 Featherstone Street, London EC1Y 8RT.
Tel: 020 7251 6333
Helpline: 020 7251 6580
www.womenshealthlondon.org.uk
(Counselling service and advice line for women suffering from gynaecological and obstetric disorders and women facing a hysterectomy.)

National charities for individual illnesses and self-help group contacts

Action for ME, 4 Deans Court, St Paul's Churchyard, London EC4V 5AA.
Tel: 020 7329 2299
www.afme.org.uk

AFASIC, 69–85 Old Street, London EC1V 9HX.
Tel: 020 7841 8900
Helpline: 0845 355 5577
www.afasic.org.uk
(For people with speech and language impairments.)

Al-Anon Family Groups UK and Eire, 61 Great Dover Street, London SE1 4YF.
Tel: 020 7403 0888 – 24-hour confidential service
www.hexnet.co.uk-alanon
(For families and friends of problem drinkers.)

Alcoholics Anonymous (AA), PO Box 1, Stonebow House, Stonebow, York YO1 7NJ.
Tel: 01904 644026 (admin)
Helpline: 0845 7697555
www.alcoholics-anonymous.org.uk

Alzheimer's Society, Gordon House, 10 Greencoat Place, London
SW1P 1PH.
Tel: 020 7306 0606
Helpline: 0845 3000 336
www.alzheimers.org.uk

Arthritis Care, 18 Stephenson Way, London NW1 2HD.
Tel: 020 7380 6500
Helpline: 020 7380 6555
www.arthritiscare.org.uk

Association for Post-Natal Illness, 25 Jerdan Place, London SW6
1BE.
Tel: 020 7386 0868
www.apni.org

BackCare (NBPA), 16 Elmtree Road, Teddington, Middlesex TW11
8ST.
Tel: 020 8977 5474
www.backpain.org

Breast CancerCare (BCC), Kiln House, 210 New Kings Road,
London SW6 4NZ.
Tel: 020 7384 2984
Helpline: 0808 800 6000
www.breastcancercare.org.uk

Bristol Cancer Help Centre, Grove House, Cornwallis Grove,
Clifton, Bristol BS8 4PG.
Tel: 0117 980 9500
Helpline: 0117 980 9505
www.bristolcancerhelp.org

British Allergy Foundation, 30 Bellegrove Road, Welling, Kent
DA16 3PY.
Tel: 020 8303 8525

British Association for Counselling (BAC), 1 Regent Place, Rugby,
Warwickshire CV21 2PJ.
Tel: 01788 550899
www.counselling.co.uk
(Can provide a list of counsellors near you.)

British Colostomy Association, 15 Station Road, Reading, Berkshire
RG1 1LG.
Tel: 0118 939 1537
Helpline: 0800 328 4257
www.bcass.org.uk

British Deaf Association, 1–3 Worship Street, London EC2A 2AB.
Tel: 020 7588 3520
www.bda.org.uk

British Epilepsy Association, New Anstey House, Gate Way Drive,
Yeadon, Leeds, North Yorkshire LS19 7XY.
Tel: 0113 210 8800
Helpline: 0808 800 5050
www.epilepsy.org

British Heart Foundation, 14 Fitzhardinge Street, London W1H
4DH.
Tel: 020 7935 0185
www.bhf.org.uk

British Kidney Patient Association, Bordon, Hampshire GU35 9JZ.
Tel: 01420 472021

British Tinnitus Association, 4th Floor, White Building, Fitzalan
Square, Sheffield S1 2AZ.
Tel: 0114 279 6600
Helpline: 0800 018 0527
www.tinnitus.org.uk

CancerBACUP, 3 Bath Place, Rivington Street, London EC2A 3JR.
Tel: 020 7696 9003
Helpline: 0808 800 1234 or 020 7613 2121
www.cancerbacup.org.uk

Cancerlink, 11–21 Northdown Street, London N1 9BN.
Tel: 020 7833 2818
Helpline: 0808 80 80 000
(Can refer you to relevant services.)

Changing Faces, 1–2 Junction Mews, London W2 1PN.
Tel: 020 7706 4232
www.changingfaces.co.uk
(For people who have a facial disfigurement.)

Crossroads – Caring for Carers, 10 Regent Place, Rugby, Warwick-
shire CV21 2PN.
Tel: 01788 573653
(Provides respite help for carers.)

Cruse Bereavement Care, Cruse House, 126 Sheen Road, Richmond
upon Thames, Surrey TW9 1UR.

Tel: 020 8940 4818
Helpline: 0870 167 1677
(For anyone who needs support after a bereavement.)

Dementia Care Trust, Kingsley House, Greenbank Road, Bristol BS5 6HE.
Tel: 0117 952 5325
www.dct.org.uk

Depression Alliance, 35 Westminster Bridge Road, London SE1 7JB.
Tel: 020 7633 0557
www.depressionalliance.org

Diabetes UK, 10 Queen Anne Street, London W1G 9LH.
Tel: 020 7323 1531
Helpline: 0207 462 2676
www.diabetes.org.uk

Disability Alliance, Universal House, 88–94 Wentworth Street, London E1 7SA.
Tel: 020 7247 8776
Advice line: 0207 247 8763
www.disabilityalliance.org
(Provides a welfare rights service and helplines and publishes guides to social security including the annual *Disability Rights Handbook*.)

Disabled Living Foundation, 380–384 Harrow Road, London W9 2HU.
Tel: 020 7289 6111
Helpline: 0870 603 9177
www.dlf.org.uk
(Provides impartial advice on equipment for independent living and fact sheets.)

Eating Disorders Association, First Floor, Wensum House, 103 Prince of Wales Road, Norwich NR1 1DW.
Tel: 01603 619090
Helpline: 01603 621414
www.edauk.com

Employment Opportunities for People with Disabilities, 123 Minories, London EC3N 1NT.
Tel: 020 7481 2727
www.opportunities.org

Employment Service Direct
Tel: 0845 60 60 234

Haemophilia Society, Chesterfield House, 385 Euston Road, London NW1 3AU.
Tel: 020 7380 0600
Helpline: 0800 018 6068
www.haemophilia.org.uk

Headway – The Brain Injury Association, 4 King Edward Court, King Edward Street, Nottingham NG1 1EW.
Tel: 0115 924 0800
www.headway.org.uk

Help the Aged, St James' Walk, Clerkenwell Green, London EC1R 0BE.
Tel: 020 7253 0253
Helpline: 0808 800 6565
www.helptheaged.org.uk

Holiday Care, 2nd Floor, Imperial Buildings, Victoria Road, Horley, Surrey RH6 7PZ.
Tel: 01293 771500
Helpline: 01293 776943
www.holidaycare.org.uk
(Provides information about suitable holiday accommodation for older and disabled people in the UK and abroad.)

Hospice Information Service, St Christopher's Hospice, 51–59 Lawrie Park Road, London SE26 6DZ.
Tel: 020 8778 9252
www.hospiceinformation.co.uk

Macmillan Cancer Relief, 89 Albert Embankment, London SE1 7UQ.
Tel: 020 7840 7840
Information line: 0845 601 6161
www.macmillan.org.uk

ME Association, 4 Corringham Road, Stanford-le-Hope, Essex SS17 0AH.
Tel: 01375 642466
Helpline: 01375 361013
www.meassociation.org.uk

Migraine Trust, 45 Great Ormond Street, London WC1N 3HZ.
Tel: 020 7831 4818
www.migrainetrust.org

MIND (National Association for Mental Health), Granta House,
15–19 Broadway, London E15 4BQ.
Tel: 020 8519 2122
Helpline: 0845 766 0163
www.mind.org.uk

Motor Neurone Disease Association, David Niven House, 10–15
Notre Dame Mews, Northampton NN1 2PR.
Tel: 01604 250505
Helpline: 0845 762 6262
www.mndassociation.org

Multiple Sclerosis Society of Great Britain and Northern Ireland,
MS National Centre, 372 Edgware Road, London NW2 6ND.
Tel: 020 8438 0700
Helpline: 0808 800 8000
www.mssociety.org.uk

National Association for Premenstrual Syndrome (NAPS), 2 East
Point, High Street, Seal, Kent TN15 0EG.
Tel: 01732 760011
Helpline: 01732 760012
www.pms.org.uk

National Asthma Campaign, Providence House, Providence Place,
London N1 0NT.
Tel: 020 7226 2260
Helpline: 0845 701 0203
www.asthma.org.uk

National Cancer Alliance, PO Box 579, Oxford OX4 1LB.
Tel: 01865 793566
(A campaigning charity which can provide information about cancer
specialists in your area as well as other support organizations.)

National Debtline, 318 Summer Lane, Newtown, Birmingham B19
3RL.
Tel: 0121 248 3000
Helpline: 0808 808 4000
www.birmingham-settlement.org.uk

National Council for Voluntary Organizations, Regents' Wharf,
8 All Saints Street, London N1 9RL.
Tel: 020 7713 6161
Voluntary Sector Helpdesk: 0800 2798 798
Textphone: 0800 0188111
www.ncvo-vol.org.uk

National Eczema Society, Hill House, Highgate Hill, London N19
5NA.
Tel: 020 7281 3553
Helpline: 0870 241 3604
www.eczema.org

National Endometriosis Society, 50 Westminster Palace Gardens,
Artillery Row, London SW1P 1RL.
Tel: 020 7222 2781
Helpline: 020 7222 2776
www.endo.org.uk

National Osteoporosis Society, PO Box 10, Radstock, Bath BA3
3YB.
Tel: 01761 471771
Helpline: 01761 472721
www.nos.org.uk

Pain Society, 9 Bedford Square, London WC1B 3RA.
Tel: 020 7636 2750
(Please write for information about pain clinics or treatments.)

Parkinson's Disease Society of the UK, 215 Vauxhall Bridge Road,
London SW1V 1EJ.
Tel: 020 7931 8080
Helpline: 0808 800 0303
www.parkinsons.org.uk

Phab, Summit House, Wandle Road, Croydon CR0 1DF.
Tel: 020 8667 9443
www.phabengland.org.uk
(A support group for both the physically disabled and able-bodied,
with over 270 clubs throughout the UK.)

Psoriasis Association, 7 Milton Street, Northampton NN2 7JG.
Tel: 01604 711129

RADAR (Royal Association for Disability and Rehabilitation),
12 City Forum, 250 City Road, London EC1V 8AF.
Tel: 020 7250 3222
www.radar.org.uk

Relate (National Marriage Guidance), Herbert Gray College, Little Church Street, Rugby, Warwickshire CV21 3AP.
Tel: 01788 573241
www.relate.org.uk

Royal National Institute for Deaf People (RNID), 19–23 Featherstone Street, London EC1Y 8SL.
Tel: 020 7296 8000
Helpline: voice 0808 808 0123; text 0808 808 9000
www.rnid.org.uk

Royal National Institute for the Blind (RNIB), 224 Great Portland Street, London W1N 6AA.
Tel: 020 7388 1266
Helpline: 0345 669999
www.rnib.org.uk

The Samaritans
Tel: 01753 532713
Helpline: 08457 909090
www.samaritans.org

SCOPE, 6 Market Road, London N7 9PW.
Tel: 020 7619 7100
Cerebral Palsy helpline: 0808 800 3333
www.scope.org.uk
(For people with cerebral palsy and related disabilities.)

Shaw Trust, Shaw House, Epsom Square, White Horse Business Park, Trowbridge, Wiltshire BA14 0XJ.
Tel: 01225 716300
Helpline: 01225 716350
www.shaw-trust.org.uk
(Provides advice, rehabilitation, training and supported employment for people with disabilities and long-term illness.)

Stroke Association, Stroke House, 123–127 Whitecross Street, London EC1Y 8JJ.
Tel: 020 7566 0300
Helpline: 0845 303 3100
www.stroke.org.uk

The Terrence Higgins Trust Lighthouse, 52–54 Gray's Inn Road, London WC1X 8JU.
Tel: 020 7831 0330
Helpline: 0207 242 1010
www.tht.org.uk
(Provides services for people living with HIV and AIDS.)

The Third Age Trust, 26 Harrison Street, London WC1H 8JG.
Tel: 020 7837 8838
www.u3a.org.uk
(Promotes self-help educational activities among retired people.)

Victim Support, Cranmer House, 39 Brixton Road, London SW9 6DZ.
Tel: 020 7735 9166
Helpline: 0845 3030 900
www.victimsupport.com
(Offers practical help and emotional support to victims of any crime and their relatives.)

Recommended reading

Disability and rights

Disability Rights Handbook (published by Disability Alliance annually); tel: 020 7247 8776 (minicom available).

Inspiring books about illness

Adams, Peter, *The Soul of Medicine: An Anthology of Illness and Healing*, Penguin, 1999.
Kabat-Zinn, Jon, *Full Catastrophe Living*, Piatkus, 1990.

The mind–body approach

Daniel, Dr Rosie, *Living with Cancer*, Robinson, 2000.
Gawain, Shakti, *Creative Vizualization*, Bantam, 1978.
George, Mike, *Learn to Relax*, Duncan Baird Publishers, 1998.
Holder, Jackee, *Soul Purpose*, Piatkus, 1999.
Lazarus, Judith, *Stress Relief and Relaxation Techniques*, Keats, 2000.
LeShan, Lawrence, *Cancer as a Turning Point*, Gateway, 1978.
LeShan, Lawrence, *How to Meditate*, Thorsons, 1995.
Simonton, Carl, *Getting Well Again*, Bantam, 1988.

Death and dying

Kübler-Ross, Elizabeth, *Wheel of Life*, Bantam, 1998.

Other useful self-help books

Carlson, Richard, *Stop Thinking and Start Living*, Thorsons, 1997.
McDermott, Ian, and O'Connor, Joseph, *NLP and Health*, Thorsons, 1996.
McDermott, Ian, and Shircore, Ian, *Manage Yourself, Manage Your Life*, Piatkus, 1999.

Nutrition

Clarke, Jane, *Body Foods for Life*, Weidenfeld & Nicolson, 1999.
Daniel, Dr Rosie, *Healing Foods*, Thorsons, 1996.
Kenton, Leslie, *The New Ultrahealth*, Vermilion, 2000.

Pain

McKenzie, R., *Treat Your Own Back*, Spinal Publications Ltd, 1995.
Melzack, Ronald, and Wall, Patrick, *The Challenge of Pain*, Penguin, 1996.
Shone, Neville, *Coping Successfully with Pain*, Sheldon Press, 1995.
Managing Pain, Reader's Digest, 1997.

(The Bristol Cancer Help Centre Shop may stock some of the above titles. They also stock several relaxation and meditation audio cassette tapes. Telephone 0117 980 9504 or order on line at www.bristolcancerhelp.org)

Index

INDEX